Crosswords

AURA

This edition published in 2015
by Baker & Taylor UK Ltd,
Bicester, Oxfordshire, OX26 4ST

ISBN: 978-1-78404-937-9
AD004428UK

Printed in China

1

1	■	2		3		4		5		
	■		■		■		■		■	■
6					■	7				8
	■		■	9			■		■	
10			11		■	12	13			
	■	■		■	■	■		■	■	
14		15		16	■	17		18		
	■		■	19			■		■	
20					■	21				
■	■		■		■		■		■	
22									■	

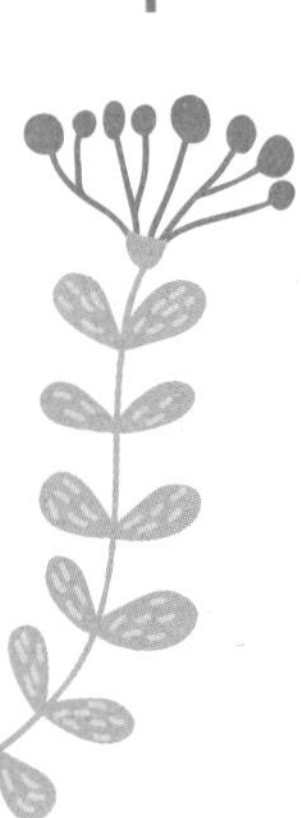

Across

2 Piece of bent wire used as a fastener (5,4)
6 Common amphibians (5)
7 Loaves of bread baked at the same time (5)
9 Number in a brace (3)
10 Line of people or vehicles (5)
12 Sharp point on a plant (5)
14 Range, scope (5)
17 Grab roughly (5)
19 Yoko ___, widow of John Lennon (3)
20 Desire strongly or persistently (5)
21 Cogwheels (5)
22 Sport with few restrictions on the moves that competitors employ (9)

Down

1 An expert or collector of ancient objects (9)
2 Woodworking tool (5)
3 Artificial gems (5)
4 Automaton (5)
5 Bingo (5)
8 People who persistently (and annoyingly) follow along (7-2)
11 Israeli submachine-gun (3)
13 Quality of a colour (3)
15 Flat spear-shaped leaf, especially of grass (5)
16 Voice qualities (5)
17 Dripping wet (5)
18 Asinine, silly (5)

2

Across

3 Navigational instrument (7)

6 Grinding tooth (5)

7 Ask earnestly (7)

8 Third letter of the Greek alphabet (5)

10 Specimen (6)

12 River of Hades (4)

14 Upper limbs (4)

17 Not established by conditioning or learning (6)

19 Rot, spoil (5)

20 Diacritical mark sometimes placed below the letter 'c' (7)

21 Cause to wither (5)

22 Young hare (7)

Down

1 Pictures (6)

2 Not elegant or graceful (6)

3 Dairy product (5)

4 Spread or diffuse through (8)

5 Jewish salutation used at meeting or parting (6)

9 Make as large or great as possible (8)

11 Dressmaking aid (3)

13 Steal something (6)

15 Phonographic disc (6)

16 Implement for cutting grass (6)

18 Make suitable for a new purpose (5)

1			2	■	3		4		5	
	■	■	6			■		■		■
7				■	8					
	■	■		■	■	■		■		■
9	10	11			12			13		■
14			■	■		■	■	15		16
■	17		18				19			
■		■		■	■	■		■	■	
20					21	■	22			
■		■		■	23			■	■	
24						■	25			

Across

1 William ___, former British prime minister (4)
3 Small, roofed building affording shade and rest (6)
6 Brazilian port, ___ de Janeiro (3)
7 Large luxurious car (abbr) (4)
8 Corrupt morally (6)
9 Combine together (10)
14 Sharp knock (3)
15 Grow older (3)
17 Writing implement with a point made of fibres (4-3,3)
20 Mutton stew with a potato topping (6)
22 Excitedly eager (4)
23 Unspecified (quantity) (3)
24 Having short sharp turns or angles (6)
25 Couch (4)

Down

1 Column (6)
2 Mythical cave-dwelling creature (5)
3 Deity (3)
4 Striped African equine (5)
5 Put under a military blockade (7)
10 Cosa Nostra members (7)
11 Large monkey (3)
12 Perform (3)
13 Bathroom fixture (3)
16 Mystery, riddle (6)
18 Administrative capital of Bolivia (2,3)
19 Takes part in a game (5)
21 Label (3)

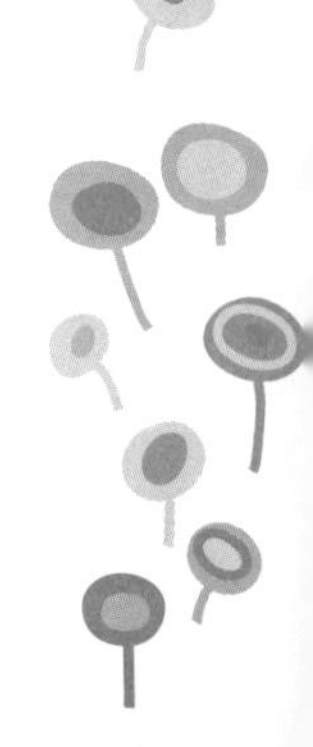

4

Across

1 Illuminated (3,2)
4 Galas (5)
8 Monarch (5)
9 Paris underground railway (5)
10 Bodily waste water (5)
11 Children's search and find game (4-3-4)
13 Emotionally unstable, disturbed (11)
15 Elephantine (5)
17 Capital of Egypt (5)
19 Skin disease affecting domestic animals (5)
20 Bellows (5)
21 Native of Stockholm, for example (5)

Down

1 Colourless fluid containing white blood cells (5)
2 Small measure of drink (3)
3 Advantages and disadvantages (4,3,4)
4 Imperial units of capacity (5,6)
5 At all times, poetically (3)
6 Neptune's spear (7)
7 Glossy, smooth (5)
12 Quandary (7)
13 Commissioned military officer (5)
14 Male bee (5)
16 Prohibit (3)
18 Frozen water (3)

5

Across

1 Totally unable to hear anything (5-4)
8 Get the better of (5)
9 Country, capital Beijing (5)
10 To the ___ degree (to the utmost) (3)
11 Ski run densely packed with snow (5)
13 Shade of blue (5)
15 Popular taste at a given time (5)
18 British author of *The Golden Notebook* (1962), ___ Lessing (5)
20 Angry dispute (3)
21 Audacity (5)
22 Follow as a result (5)
23 Taking part in hand-to-hand combat (9)

Down

2 Carries with difficulty (5)
3 Not a single person (2-3)
4 Russian country house (5)
5 French goodbye (5)
6 Qualified, capable (9)
7 Event marking an important historical change of course (9)
12 Prepare leather (3)
14 Facility where wild animals are housed for exhibition (3)
16 Inadvertent incorrectness (5)
17 Frock (5)
18 Reside (5)
19 Plant exudation (5)

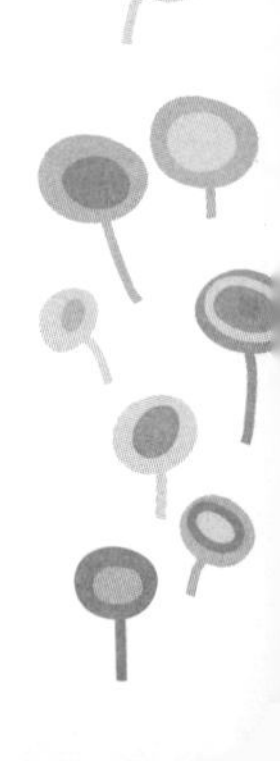

6

Across

1 Flowerless plants that reproduce by spores (5)
4 Cartoon duck often associated with Bugs Bunny (5)
7 Anticipates (7)
8 Headdress worn by a bishop (5)
9 Body of water between Israel and Jordan (4,3)
13 Absorbed, engrossed (4)
16 Despatched (4)
17 Canvas shoe with a pliable rubber sole (7)
19 Bring together (5)
20 Spectacles worn to protect the eyes (7)
21 Political organisation (5)
22 Stiff pompous gait (5)

Down

1 Agriculturalists (7)
2 Bureaucratic procedure (3,4)
3 Warhorse (5)
5 Rectifies (6)
6 Make plump (6)
10 To stretch out (3)
11 Meeting for an exchange of ideas (7)
12 One who denies the existence of God (7)
14 Fine, silky hair, used to make garments (6)
15 Educated (6)
18 Corrodes, as with metal affected by water (5)

1		2		3	■	4		5		6
	■		■		■		■		■	
7										
	■		■		■		■		■	
8	9		10	■	11		12		13	
■		■		■		■		■		■
14		15		16		■	17	18		19
	■		■		■	20	■		■	
21										
	■		■		■		■		■	
22					■	23				

7

Across

1 General conscious awareness (5)
4 Enclosures for pets (5)
7 Serving to identify a species or group (11)
8 Claims (4)
11 Vast, sandy region (6)
14 Flow freely and abundantly (6)
17 Behaves in a particular way (4)
21 Dehydrating, boiling away (11)
22 Appreciation (5)
23 Grinds (5)

Down

1 Outer surfaces of an object (5)
2 Inquisitive (5)
3 Extremely wicked (4)
4 Periodically repeated sequence (5)
5 Direct (5)
6 Paid out money (5)
9 Painting, sculpture, etc (3)
10 That girl (3)
11 Badly lit (3)
12 Division of an ocean (3)
13 Common rodent (3)
14 Sugary (5)
15 Interprets words (5)
16 Higher up (5)
18 Cool down (5)
19 Puts a name to (5)
20 Inner surface of the hand (4)

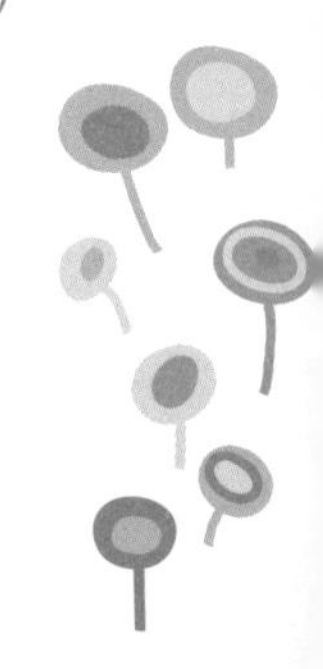

8

Across

1 Haywire, awry (5)
5 Female pig (3)
7 US state, capital Boise (5)
8 Russian prison camp for political prisoners (5)
9 Church instrument (5)
10 Stretchy fabric (7)
13 Wealthy and privileged people (coll) (3,4)
15 Emit an odour (5)
16 Stringed instrument of Indian origin (5)
17 Construct (a building) (5)
18 Ancient (3)
19 Imperial units of length (5)

Down

1 Fisherman (6)
2 Rude (3-8)
3 The faculty of vision (5)
4 Mayhem (5)
5 Greatly desired (6,5)
6 Notify of danger (4)
11 Brother of George Gershwin (3)
12 Egyptian god of the underworld (6)
13 Group of ships (5)
14 Appetising (5)
15 Alone (4)

9

Across

1 Hold up (5)
4 Make jokes (4)
6 Elaborate song for a solo voice (4)
8 Unit of length (4)
10 Second-hand (4)
12 Declaration (9)
14 Having two parts (4)
16 Providing or supporting with money (9)
18 Seethe (4)
19 Flourished, especially financially (9)
23 Travel permit (4)
24 Musical finale (4)
25 French word for Christmas (4)
26 Badgers' den (4)
27 Connecting parts of a chain (5)

Down

1 Canine creatures (4)
2 Tibetan or Mongolian priest (4)
3 US university (4)
4 Affected by envy, resentment or cynicism (9)
5 Ebbing and flowing (5)
7 Recall the past (9)
9 Person who walks from place to place (9)
11 Knock senseless (4)
13 Bean curd (4)
15 Fit of shivering or shaking (4)
17 Mischievous fairies (4)
18 Court game resembling handball (5)
20 Survey of opinions (4)
21 Drizzle (4)
22 Expires (4)

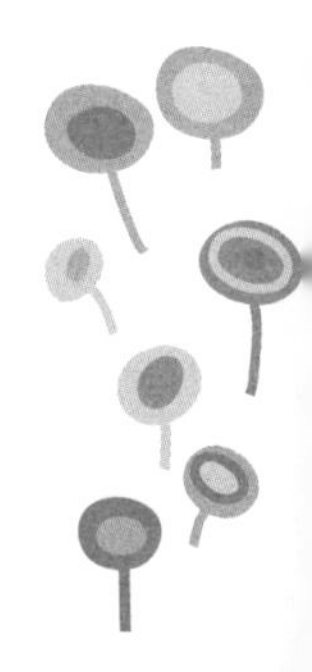

10

Across

1 State capital of Western Australia (5)
3 Oddment (5)
6 Cook slowly in liquid (4)
8 Piece of material inset to enlarge a garment (6)
10 Line spoken by an actor to the audience (5)
12 Numbered page (5)
14 Cocktail of vermouth and gin (7)
15 Ingrained dirt (5)
16 Demands (5)
18 Latin American country (6)
19 Celebrity (4)
20 Special occasion (5)
21 Fetch (5)

Down

1 Shaped and dried dough (5)
2 Pull (vehicles) (3)
3 Savoury mixture cooked in a turkey, for example (8)
4 Recovering readily from adversity (9)
5 Paved area that adjoins a house (5)
7 Do away with (9)
9 Abandoned, falling in ruins (8)
11 Female parent of an animal (3)
13 A person in general (3)
15 Clark ____, film actor (1901–60) (5)
17 Raise one's shoulders to indicate indifference (5)
19 Form of address to a man (3)

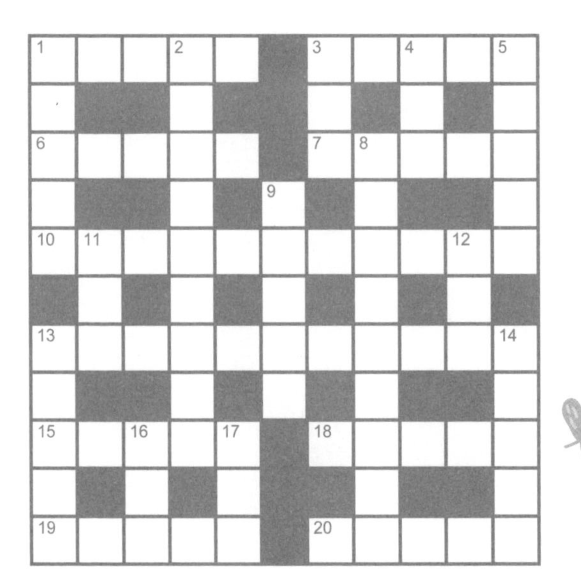

11

Across

1 Tiny morsel of bread or cake (5)
3 European country (5)
6 Country, capital New Delhi (5)
7 Harmless tropical house-lizard (5)
10 Device operated by the insertion of a coin (4,7)
13 Pointed biting tool (6,5)
15 Turn red with embarrassment (5)
18 Garden tool for cutting grass on lawns (5)
19 Select by a vote (5)
20 Tower supporting high-tension wires (5)

Down

1 Counters used to represent money when gambling (5)
2 Keeps in a certain state (9)
3 Droop (3)
4 Joan of ___, French heroine (3)
5 Loop formed in a cord or rope (5)
8 Cultural anthropology (9)
9 Maurice ___, French composer (1875–1937) (5)
11 Meadow (3)
12 Piece of metal with a hole used to secure a bolt (3)
13 Nautical unit of depth (5)
14 Wading bird with a long neck (5)
16 Consumption (3)
17 Very warm (3)

12

Across

1 Garment hanging from the waist (5)
3 Substance used for writing on a blackboard (5)
7 Utensil used to shred cheese, etc (6)
9 Eastern staple foodstuff (4)
10 Recede (3)
12 Chopped (4)
13 Alleviated (5)
15 Diffident (3)
17 Proportion (5)
19 Hindu or Buddhist religious leader (4)
21 Flightless bird (3)
22 Prayer-ending word (4)
23 Long seat (6)
25 Coffee-chocolate drink (5)
26 Item of cutlery (5)

Down

1 Communicate silently (6)
2 Deep groove (3)
4 Aromatic plants used in cookery (5)
5 Longitudinal beam of the hull of a ship (4)
6 Structure built in branches for children to play in (4,5)
8 Central area of an ancient Roman amphitheatre (5)
11 Alcove (3)
14 Spew forth lava and rocks (5)
15 Card in a mobile phone (inits) (3)
16 Dish used for serving soup (6)
18 Last Commandment (5)
20 Date-producing tree (4)
24 Pinnacle (3)

1		2			3	■	4	■	5	■
	■		■	■	6					
7				■		■		■		■
	■		■	8		9				
10	11		■		■		■	■		■
12								13		14
■		■	■		■		■	15		
16			17		18		■		■	
■		■		■		■	19			
20						■	■		■	
■		■		■	21					

13

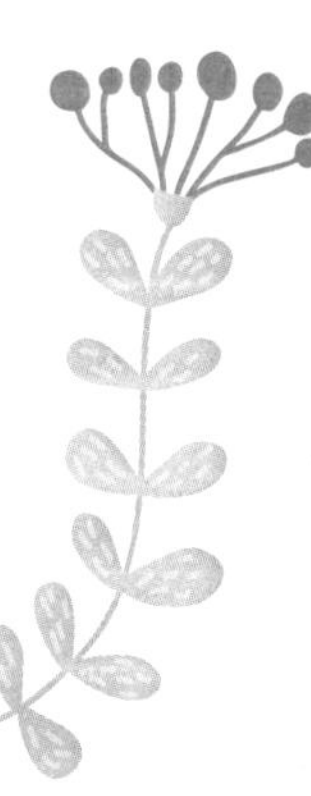

Across

1 Expresses gratitude (6)

6 Alternative (6)

7 Fluctuate (4)

8 US legislator (7)

10 Lick up (3)

12 Wavelengths shorter than light but longer than X-rays (11)

15 Source of metal (3)

16 In a relaxed manner, not rigid (7)

19 Grassy garden area (4)

20 Grinding teeth (6)

21 Emphasise (6)

Down

1 Group of coral islands in Micronesia (6)

2 Exceedingly sudden and unexpected (6)

3 Painful (4)

4 Highest volcano in Europe (4)

5 Public medical examiner (7)

8 Look at intently (5)

9 Cacophonous (5)

11 Intoxicating liquor (7)

13 Discover the site of (6)

14 Game associated with Wimbledon (6)

17 Expectorated (4)

18 Deprivation (4)

14

Across

1 Involving financial matters (6)

6 Less difficult (6)

7 Spice made from the covering of the nutmeg (4)

8 Mother superior (6)

10 Rope used to restrain an animal (5)

13 Small sack of dried seeds used in children's games (7)

15 Level betting (5)

16 Abundance of material possessions and resources (6)

18 Hackney carriage (4)

19 Close of day (6)

20 Not faint or feeble (6)

Down

1 Acquaint, make conversant with (11)

2 Dairy product (6)

3 Fictional princess in the *Star Wars* films (4)

4 Total distance covered by a motor vehicle (7)

5 Entering unlawfully on someone's property (11)

9 Live-action film about a piglet (4)

11 Leave without permission (7)

12 Lean-fleshed fish similar to cod (4)

14 Icon representing a person, used in internet chat and games (6)

17 Solidifies (4)

15

1	■	2	■	3	■	4		5		6
7							■		■	
	■		■		■		■		■	
8			9		■	10	11			
	■	12			■	■		■	■	
■	13					14		15		■
16	■	■		■	■	17			■	18
19		20		21	■	22				
	■		■		■		■		■	
	■		■	23						
24					■		■		■	

Across

4 Contest between opposing teams (5)
7 State of the world as it truly is (7)
8 Drivers' stopover (5)
10 Capital of Vietnam (5)
12 False statement (3)
13 Isolate in a discriminatory way (9)
17 Stretch (3)
19 Planet in our solar system (5)
22 Long (for) (5)
23 Keep from happening (7)
24 Subdivision of an act of a play (5)

Down

1 Rigid part of a bicycle (5)
2 Bovine animals (6)
3 Murderer (6)
4 Traditional story (4)
5 Ripped (4)
6 Custom (5)
9 Number of sides in an octagon (5)
11 Not in a state of sleep (5)
14 Natural spring that gives out steam (6)
15 Service of china or silverware, used at table (3,3)
16 Lone Star State of the USA (5)
18 Links together, as with needles and wool (5)
20 Contest of speed (4)
21 Expect and wish (4)

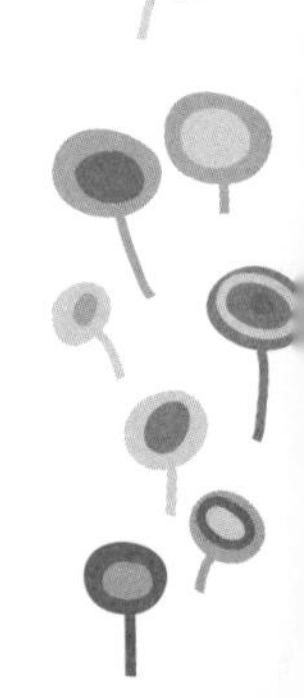

16

Across

1 Roughly-built hut (5)
4 Make angry (5)
7 Peter Paul ___, baroque painter (1577–1640) (6)
9 Peruse text (4)
11 Place of safety or sanctuary (5)
12 Make unauthorised alterations (6)
14 Collection of miscellaneous things (4)
16 Female horse (4)
19 Craft for transportation by water (6)
21 Triangular part of a wall (5)
22 Country road (4)
23 Tiny (6)
25 Loans out (5)
26 Control board (5)

Down

1 One of several parallel layers of material (7)
2 Set of recordings, especially musical (5)
3 Range of knowledge (3)
5 Apprehensive, anxious (7)
6 Native of Muscat, for example (5)
8 Wither, especially due to loss of moisture (7)
10 Slippery fish (3)
13 Sum of money allotted by a cathedral to a canon (7)
15 Mineral source (3,4)
17 Semi-precious stone (5)
18 Directed or controlled (3)
20 Smooth fabric (5)
24 Little rascal (3)

1			2		■	3	4			5
	■	■		■	6	■		■	■	
7		8				■	9			
	■		■	■		■		■	■	
10				11		12		13		■
	■		■	14			■		■	15
■	16		17							
18	■	■		■		■	■		■	
19				■	20		21			
	■	■		■		■		■	■	
22					■	23				

17

Across

1 Employee who keeps records or accounts (5)

3 Fictitious, untrue (5)

7 More orderly (6)

9 Unit of length (4)

10 Engaging in histrionic pretence (4-6)

14 Professional price (3)

16 Large hemispherical brass or copper percussion instrument (10)

19 Excavates (4)

20 Hand-held piece of armour (6)

22 Devoid of clothing (5)

23 Travel on ice (5)

Down

1 Cockpit cover (6)

2 Decompose (3)

4 Excuse for failure (5)

5 Reverberation (4)

6 Having incalculable monetary worth (9)

8 Become less intense (5)

11 Astern (3)

12 Golf peg (3)

13 Hospital worker (5)

15 Blur (6)

17 Discernment (5)

18 Chief port of Yemen (4)

21 Vex (3)

18

Across

1 Cuts into pieces (5)

4 Adjust a camera lens so as to get a sharp image (5)

7 Artist's workroom (7)

8 Popular vegetable (3)

9 Digress (5)

11 Call to mind (5)

12 Fraction equal to twenty per cent (5)

14 Emergence (5)

15 *The Catcher in the ___*, J D Salinger novel (3)

16 Bridge consisting of a series of arches (7)

18 Locations (5)

19 Seat (5)

Down

1 Distinctive heraldic bearings or shields (5,2,4)

2 Be in debt (3)

3 Lustrous (5)

4 Play characterised by broad satire (5)

5 Ample, plentiful (7)

6 Portable device that warms the air in a room (5,6)

10 Act like a mirror (7)

13 Homes for bees (5)

14 ___ Asimov, science-fiction writer (5)

17 Country, capital Washington DC (inits) (3)

19

Across

1 State in New England, USA (5,6)
7 Celebration of the Eucharist (4)
8 Venerate (6)
9 Pedal digit (3)
11 Composed for or sung by a choir (6)
13 Large island of the Inner Hebrides (4)
14 Anticipate (7)
16 Chancy (coll) (4)
17 Skilled, proficient (6)
19 Cash machine outside a bank (inits) (3)
20 English author of satirical novels, ___ Waugh (6)
21 Yob deterrent (inits) (4)
22 Became calmer (7,4)

Down

2 Tract of level wasteland (5)
3 Annihilate (7)
4 State of being of no importance (11)
5 Wide streets (7)
6 Lived, resided (7)
10 Device used to propel a boat (3)
11 Stoneworking tools (7)
12 Eccentric, unconventional (7)
13 Imaginary sea nymph (7)
15 Film props and scenery (3)
18 Hinge joint in the arm (5)

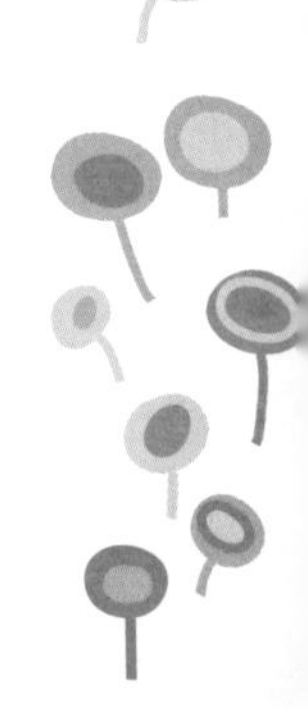

20

Across

1 Demand as rightful (5)
4 Largest artery of the body (5)
7 Sparkle (7)
9 Military action in which besieged troops burst forth from their position (6)
10 Storage locker (7)
13 Scottish valley (4)
16 Lower part of an interior wall (4)
17 Canvas receptacle from which a horse can feed (7)
19 Laminated metamorphic rock similar to granite (6)
20 Body of water into which the River Jordan flows (4,3)
21 ___ Cup, golf tournament played every two years (5)
22 Rental contract (5)

Down

1 Give over to another for safekeeping (7)
2 Accumulates (7)
3 Sorcery (5)
5 Offer to pay a higher price for (6)
6 Layered (6)
8 Unwanted discharge of a fluid (7)
11 Country, capital Windhoek (7)
12 Shaved crown of a monk's head (7)
14 In need of company (6)
15 Knitting tool (6)
18 Twist into a state of deformity (5)

21

1			2	■	3				4	
	■	■	5			■	■	■		■
6				■	7		8			
	■	■		■	■	■		■		■
9		10			11			12		■
	■		■	■		■	■		■	13
■	14		15				16			
■		■		■	■	■		■	■	
17					18	■	19			
■		■	■	■	20			■	■	
21						■	22			

Across

1 Roman cloak (4)
3 Ambush (6)
5 Insect (3)
6 House attached to one other (4)
7 Item of headgear with a tall crown (3,3)
9 Downplay (10)
14 Living quarters in the bow of a merchant ship (10)
17 Gigantic African and Australian tree with edible fruits (6)
19 In the centre of (4)
20 Hand tool used to mark surfaces (3)
21 Decapitate (6)
22 Unemployment benefit (4)

Down

1 Paper handkerchief (6)
2 Endure (5)
3 Soaked with a liquid (3)
4 Quickly (5)
8 Pulse vegetable (3)
10 Singing couple (3)
11 Intentionally so written (used after a printed word) (3)
12 Small measure of drink (3)
13 Pine leaf (6)
14 Blaze (5)
15 Subject to laughter or ridicule (3)
16 Burn with steam (5)
18 Unsound (3)

22

Across

1 Choral work (5)

4 Of limited quantity (5)

7 Cry expressing disapproval (7)

8 Took a chair (3)

9 Beauty parlour (5)

11 Male duck (5)

12 Discontinue (5)

14 Shout of approval (5)

16 Male child (3)

17 Thankless wretch (7)

19 Bout, period of indulgence (5)

20 Have another go (5)

Down

1 Protective secretion of bodily membranes (5)

2 Small insectivorous bird (3)

3 Form of transport that runs on a track (5)

4 Dish of lettuce, tomatoes, cucumber, etc (5)

5 Satisfy (thirst) (7)

6 Offering of a tenth part of some personal income (5)

10 Trainee (7)

12 Prices (5)

13 Deport from a country (5)

14 Roll of tobacco (5)

15 Thin-toned (5)

18 Towards the rear (3)

23

1		2			3	■	4	■	5	■
	■		■	■	6					
7				■		■		■		■
	■		■	8		9		10		11
12					■	13				
	■		■	14			■		■	
15	16		17		■	18				
19					20		■		■	
■		■		■		■	21			
22						■	■		■	
■		■		■	23					

Across

1 Pail (6)
6 Tomboy (6)
7 Uncommon (4)
8 Painters, sculptors, etc (7)
12 Dissident (5)
13 Bring up (5)
14 Not of the clergy (3)
15 Point in the time of a cycle (5)
18 Proprietor (5)
19 Idyllically calm and peaceful (7)
21 Price (4)
22 Come into possession of (6)
23 In a tidy and ordered way (6)

Down

1 Chart showing comparative quantities by means of rectangular blocks of varying proportional height (3,5)
2 Intellectual (8)
3 Norse deity (4)
4 Middle Eastern country (5)
5 Divisions of a dollar (5)
8 Narrow backstreet (5)
9 Don a garment before purchase (3,2)
10 Guide that shows the way (8)
11 In a covert manner (8)
16 Emerge from an egg (5)
17 Dandruff (5)
20 Unlocked (4)

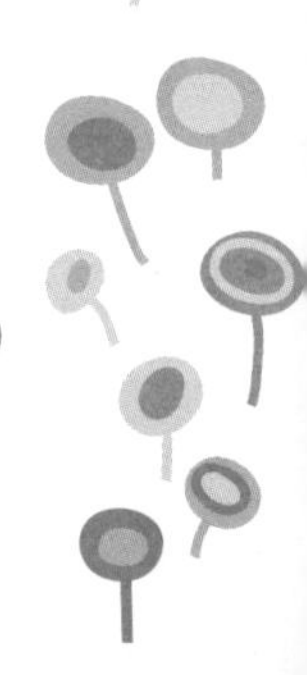

24

Across

1 Hackney carriage (4)

3 River that flows through Bonn (5)

6 Africa's longest river (4)

7 Mats (4)

9 Bar chart representing a frequency distribution (9)

11 Put pen to paper (5)

12 Reach a desired goal (7)

15 Partially melted snow (5)

17 Bona fide (9)

18 Give up (4)

19 ___ Strauss, jeans manufacturer (4)

20 Child's nurse (5)

21 Brass instrument (4)

Down

1 Projected through the air (5)

2 Being in the original position (2,4)

3 Most distant and isolated (8)

4 Cause to come to know personally (9)

5 Adversary, foe (5)

8 Deserted settlement (5,4)

10 In a covert manner (8)

13 Derive by reason (6)

14 Breakfast rasher (5)

16 Scavenging carnivore (5)

25

Across

1 Gemstone (5)
4 Enter (data or a program) into a computer (5)
8 Bathroom fixtures (4)
9 Overabundance (6)
10 Nervous twitch (3)
11 Couch (4)
13 US coin (4)
14 Embarrassed (7)
15 Small gentle horse (4)
16 Withered (4)
17 Fluid used for writing (3)
18 Scottish landowners (6)
19 Garments, clothes generally (4)
21 After the expected time (5)
22 Cider fruit (5)

Down

2 Epoch, age (3)
3 Rapture (7)
5 Command, control (7)
6 Lacking flavour (9)
7 Device with moving parts (9)
8 Aviator hired to fly experimental aeroplanes in designed manoeuvres (4,5)
12 More decorative (7)
13 Area of a computer monitor on which icons and windows appear (7)
20 Mousse applied to the hair (3)

26

Across

1 Mildewed (5)
4 Suspicious, not as expected (coll) (5)
7 Type of haircut (6)
9 Girdle (4)
10 Mud or small rocks deposited in an estuary (4)
11 Stylish (4)
13 As well (4)
15 Manor-house with lands adjacent to it not let out to tenants (7)
16 Abominable snowman (4)
17 27th president of the USA (4)
19 Put down (4)
21 Type of food shop (abbr) (4)
22 Migratory shorebird (6)
23 Irish word for a lake (5)
24 Asian pepper plant (5)

Down

1 Imitate (5)
2 Helmut ___, former chancellor of Germany (7)
3 Deviates erratically from a set course (4)
5 Immediate (7)
6 Popular web portal (5)
8 Relating to the motion of material bodies (7)
12 Overhead surface of a room (7)
14 Brochure (7)
16 Alpine vocal call (5)
18 Drying cloth (5)
20 Unable to speak (4)

27

Across

1 Tiny (5)
4 Young girl (4)
6 Keen on (4)
8 Not censored (5)
9 Bathroom pipes and fixtures (8)
12 Stew (4)
13 City in western Germany (5)
15 Arboreal mammal (5)
17 Native of Warsaw, for example (4)
19 Cooking (meat) by dry heat in an oven (8)
21 Assistants (5)
22 Marine mammal (4)
23 Faucets (4)
24 Skin disease affecting domestic animals (5)

Down

1 Hole in which water has collected (4)
2 Cancel (5)
3 State of being disregarded or forgotten (5)
4 Venture involving risk but promising great rewards (4,4)
5 Lucifer (5)
7 Succession of notes forming a distinctive sequence (4)
10 Be lazy or idle (4)
11 Kept woman (8)
14 Constant (4)
15 Begin (5)
16 Flexible pipe for conveying a liquid (4)
17 Religious song (5)
18 Animate (5)
20 Great merriment (4)

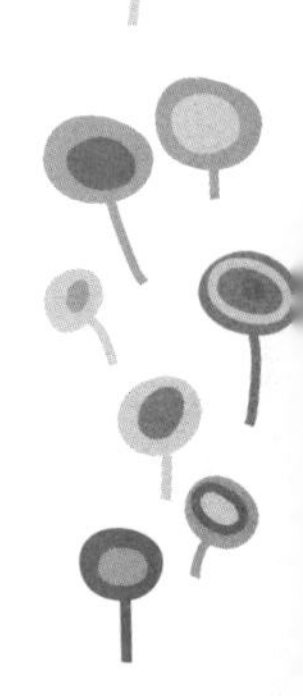

28

Across

1 Bell of the clock associated with the UK's Houses of Parliament (3,3)

6 Foolhardy (6)

7 Ski race over a winding course (6)

8 Armed fight (6)

10 Pandemonium (5)

13 Itinerant Australian labourer (7)

16 Establish (3,2)

18 Being in the original position (2,4)

20 Burns with steam (6)

21 Glimpse (6)

22 Profoundly (6)

Down

1 Fundamental (5)

2 Catch the wind (6)

3 Insensitive, dull to pain (4)

4 Far off (7)

5 Native American tent (5)

9 Charitable gifts (4)

11 In the customary manner (2,5)

12 Condiment, sodium chloride (4)

14 Supply or impregnate with oxygen (6)

15 Where the sides of a ship curve in to form the bottom (5)

17 Meat pie (5)

19 Taken advantage of (4)

29

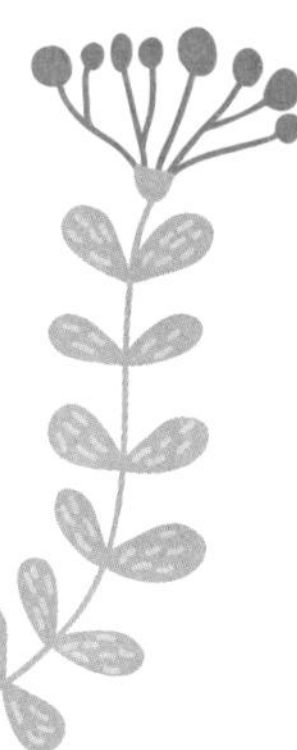

1		2		3	■	■	4	5		6
	■		■	7					■	
8	9		■		■	■	10			
11					12	■		■	■	
■		■	■	13		14			15	
■		■	16					■		■
17							■	■		■
	■	■		■	18			19		20
21		22		■	■		■	23		
	■	24					■		■	
25				■	■	26				

Across

1 Watery fluid of the blood (5)
4 Line formed by joining two pieces (4)
7 Find repugnant (5)
8 Pixie (3)
10 Male sheep (4)
11 Isolated fact considered separately from the whole (6)
13 Inhabitant of a town or community (7)
16 Rescued (5)
17 Bewilder (7)
18 Not faint or feeble (6)
21 Yearn (for) (4)
23 Consumed (3)
24 Projecting bay window (5)
25 Expect and wish (4)
26 Distinctive spirit of a culture (5)

Down

1 Garden toolhouse (4)
2 Vessel made of wooden planks (4)
3 Spellbinding, mysterious (7)
4 Seedy (6)
5 Time period (3)
6 Craftsman who works with stone (5)
9 Barrier constructed to keep out the sea (5)
12 Exists (5)
14 Cloth, fabric (7)
15 Special occasion (5)
16 Orb, globe (6)
17 Downy juicy fruit (5)
19 Solemn promise (4)
20 Obtains (4)
22 Plant with flowers used in brewing (3)

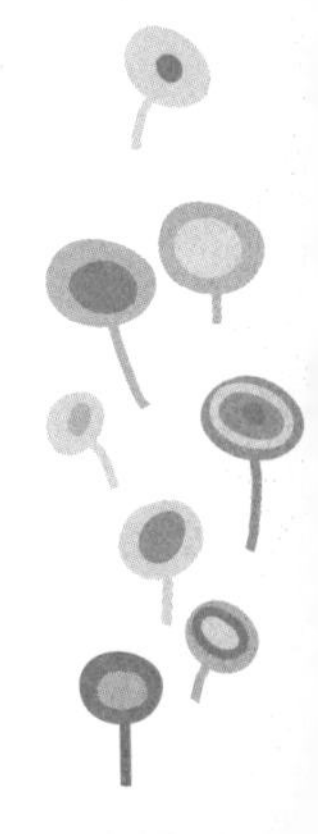

30

Across

1 Racket (5)
3 Plants often found in arid regions of the world (5)
6 Comes to terms (with) (5)
9 Scour (5)
10 Respond (5)
12 Exaggerate to an excessive degree (6)
13 Block of soap (4)
14 Grime (4)
15 Brine-cured (6)
19 Aladdin's spirit (5)
20 Country, capital Accra (5)
21 Irritable (5)
22 One sixteenth of a pound (5)
23 Durable aromatic wood (5)

Down

1 Tortilla chip topped with cheese and chilli pepper (5)
2 Absolute (5)
3 Actors in a play (4)
4 Miguel de ___, Spanish writer best remembered for *Don Quixote* (9)
5 Permeate (5)
7 Determine beforehand (9)
8 Mournful (3)
11 Clump of trees (5)
14 Quietly in concealment (coll) (5)
16 Little insect (3)
17 Belgian city (5)
18 Appliance that removes moisture (5)
19 Contributed (4)

31

1		2		3		4		5		6
	■		■		■		■		■	
7					■	8				
	■		■	9			■		■	
10			11		■	12	13			
	■	■		■	■	■		■	■	
14		15		16	■	17		18		
	■		■	19			■		■	
20					■	21				
	■		■		■		■		■	
22										

Across

1 Concise and full of meaning (11)
7 Minute particles of matter (5)
8 Anxious (5)
9 Reverence (3)
10 Mineral used as an abrasive (5)
12 Device used to connect computers by a telephone line (5)
14 In the centre of (5)
17 Lucifer (5)
19 Irritate (3)
20 Thespian (5)
21 Boredom (5)
22 Pottery made of porous clay fired at low heat (11)

Down

1 Artificially arrange so as to have a particular effect (5-6)
2 Loop formed in a cord or rope (5)
3 Literary composition (5)
4 Carved pole associated with native North Americans (5)
5 Possessed (5)
6 Type of railway locomotive (5,6)
11 Directed or controlled (3)
13 Reproductive cells (3)
15 Further from the middle (5)
16 Distance around a person's body (5)
17 Coil of knitting wool (5)
18 Kingdom in the South Pacific (5)

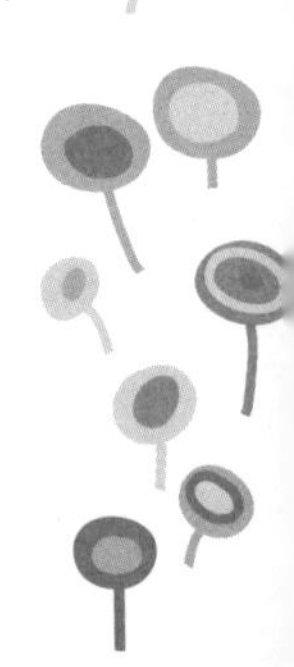

32

Across

1 Wounding or wittily pointed remarks (5)
4 Noxious gases (5)
8 British county dissolved in 1996 (4)
9 Garden pest (4)
10 Cruel dictator (6)
11 Sluggish (4)
12 Jar of glass or porcelain (4)
13 Affect with wonder (5)
14 Lengthy (4)
16 Embedded part (4)
18 Halogen element (6)
19 Thomas ___, German writer (1875–1955) (4)
20 Country, capital Teheran (4)
21 Prime minister of India from 1947 to 1964 (5)
22 Heavenly messenger (5)

Down

2 Blacksmith's block (5)
3 Popular trend that attracts growing support (9)
5 Island in the Mediterranean (5)
6 Drop a hint (7)
7 Imagine, see in one's mind (9)
9 Monarch (9)
11 Bathsheba's son (7)
15 Coming next after the eighth (5)
17 Give a speech (5)

33

1			2		3	■	■	4	■	5
	■	■		■	6					
7				■		■	■		■	
	■	■	8	9		10				
11		12					■		■	
■	■		■		■		■		■	■
13	■		■	14	15		16			17
18								■	■	
	■		■	■		■	19			
20						■		■	■	
	■		■	■	21					

Across

1 Construction built by a spider (6)

6 Long-bodied reptile (6)

7 Substantive word (4)

8 Engage in plotting (8)

11 It's said to make the heart grow fonder (7)

14 Component part (7)

18 Sound made by a mobile phone (8)

19 Remove (4)

20 Counting frame (6)

21 The act of coming out (6)

Down

1 Dance involving a long line of people (5)

2 Cringe (5)

3 Highest peak in the Alps, Mont ___ (5)

4 Afternoon theatrical performance (7)

5 More peculiar (5)

9 Beginning of an offensive (5)

10 Number considered lucky (5)

12 Public outrage (7)

13 Off-white colour (5)

15 At liberty (5)

16 Instrument for measuring a quantity (5)

17 Moves in large numbers, swarms (5)

34

1			2		■	■	3	4		5
	■	■		■	6				■	
7				8		■	9			
	■	■	10			■	■		■	
11		12				■	13			
	■		■	14		15	■		■	
16				■	17		18			
	■		■	■	19			■	■	
20			21	■	22					
	■	23				■		■	■	
24				■	■	25				

Across

1 Make parallel (5)
3 Stated (4)
6 Notify of danger (4)
7 Derek ___, British actor who was knighted in 1994 (6)
9 Egyptian goddess (4)
10 Tub (3)
11 Arid region (6)
13 Word that denotes an action (4)
14 Take an exam (3)
16 Birthday missive (4)
17 Discontinued (6)
19 Mischievous little fairy (3)
20 Shade of green-blue (4)
22 Globe (6)
23 Appear (4)
24 Dry biscuit, a teething aid (4)
25 Authoritative proclamation (5)

Down

1 One who studies and settles conflicts and disputes (11)
2 Item worn on the hand (5)
3 ___ Lanka, country (3)
4 Replies (7)
5 Unruly (11)
6 Clever joke (9)
8 Establishments where alcoholic drinks are served (4)
12 Do something to a greater degree (7)
15 Short-term worker (abbr) (4)
18 Greenfly, for instance (5)
21 Basic unit of money in Albania (3)

1				2	■	3	■	4		5
	■	■	■	6					■	
7		8			■		■		■	
	■		■		■	9				
10					11		■		■	■
	■		■	■		■	■		■	12
■	■		■	13		14				
15					■		■		■	
	■		■		■	16				
	■	17					■	■	■	
18			■		■	19				

35

Across

1 Missives used as birthday or Christmas greetings (5)

4 Female of domestic cattle (3)

6 Dire (5)

7 Lawful, legitimate (5)

9 US state in the Rocky Mountains (5)

10 Throat (7)

13 It's said to make the heart grow fonder (7)

15 Pasture (5)

16 Construct (a building) (5)

17 Equally (5)

18 Number (3)

19 Automobile race run over public roads (5)

Down

1 Civil and religious leader of a Muslim state (6)

2 Grilled food on a skewer, served with peanut sauce (5)

3 Stick on (5)

4 Permission (9)

5 Chronic drinker (sl) (4)

8 One who pretends to have special knowledge or ability (9)

11 Seize suddenly (3)

12 In a tidy and ordered way (6)

13 Jelly based on fish or meat stock (5)

14 Guide a vessel (5)

15 Person's manner of walking, pace (4)

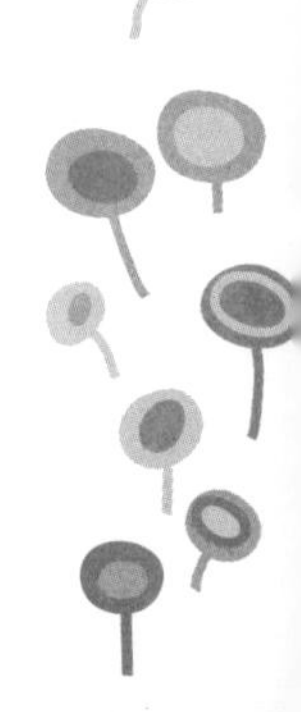

36

Across

1 Pigment prepared from the ink of cuttlefishes (5)

4 Clench, clutch tightly (5)

7 Restrain (7)

8 Beast of burden (3)

9 Types, varieties (5)

11 Root vegetable (5)

12 Tip at an angle (5)

14 Bushy plant (5)

16 Towards the rear (3)

17 Acquired knowledge (7)

19 Suggestive of the supernatural (5)

20 Compel (5)

Down

1 Draws in by a vacuum (5)

2 Metal cooking vessel (3)

3 Assumed name (5)

4 Conjecture (5)

5 Non-professional (7)

6 Ski run densely packed with snow (5)

10 Nuclear plant (7)

12 Judder (5)

13 Fine net used for veils (5)

14 Woollen item worn about the neck (5)

15 Emblem (5)

18 Not either (3)

37

Across

1 Marked by friendly companionship with others (6)

6 Detestable (6)

7 Unspecified items (6)

9 Artist's workroom (7)

10 Prepares for printing (5)

12 Acutely insightful and wise (7)

17 Greek author of fables (5)

18 Pastoral (7)

20 Nation between India and China (6)

21 Overland journey by hunters (6)

22 Shriek (6)

Down

1 Small sofa (6)

2 Total disaster (6)

3 Disorientated (4)

4 Aircraft with two wings, one above the other (7)

5 Continental quilt (5)

8 Short intake of breath (4)

11 Group of people attractively arranged (7)

13 Every one (4)

14 Species of fly that transmits sleeping sickness (6)

15 Name derived from the name of a person (6)

16 ___ Allan Poe, author (5)

19 Wading bird (4)

38

Across

1 Hoodlum (4)
3 Conclude by reasoning (5)
6 Kitchen appliance (4)
7 Arm bone (4)
9 Expiation (9)
10 Not having a protective covering (4)
11 Performance (7)
15 Anon (4)
17 Dependent upon or characterised by chance (3-2-4)
18 Long fishes (4)
19 Looks (4)
20 Conjecture (5)
21 Slipped smoothly (4)

Down

1 Digit of the hand (5)
2 Pointed beard (6)
3 Devise (6)
4 Keep from happening, make impossible (9)
5 Corroded (5)
8 Message that tells the particulars of an act or occurrence (9)
12 Stroke lovingly (6)
13 Appraise (6)
14 Item (5)
16 Pried (5)

39

Across

1 Relating to capital letters (5,4)
8 South American cud-chewing animal (5)
9 Fourth letter of the Greek alphabet (5)
10 Catch sight of (3)
11 Run off to marry (5)
13 Took in liquid (5)
15 Doglike nocturnal mammal (5)
18 Love affair (5)
20 Chap (3)
21 Relating to the countryside (5)
22 Impurities left in the final drops of a liquid (5)
23 Public court case in which the guilt of the defendant has already been decided (4,5)

Down

2 Keyboard instrument (5)
3 Rub out (5)
4 Encrypted (5)
5 Spicy sauce to accompany Mexican food (5)
6 Long valveless wooden wind instrument used for signalling in the mountains (9)
7 Personification of icy or wintry weather (4,5)
12 Livestock enclosure (3)
14 Edge, border (3)
16 Home planet (5)
17 Permit (5)
18 Common viper (5)
19 Last letter of the Greek alphabet (5)

40

Across

1 Sailor of legend, who undertook seven voyages (6)

6 Nuclear (6)

8 Unenclosed space outdoors (4,3)

9 Gesture (4)

10 Inexpensive (5)

13 Rope used to brace a tent (3)

14 Speak with others about (7)

16 Indian honorific title (3)

17 Eye covering (5)

19 Diplomacy (4)

21 Skyline (7)

22 Portuguese islands in the Atlantic (6)

23 Drink made of lemonade and beer (6)

Down

1 Unemotional person (5)

2 Art of growing miniature trees (6)

3 Raised platform (4)

4 Surrounded by (7)

5 Saying: "The real ___", the genuine article (5)

7 Cause to stumble (4,2)

11 Issue of a newspaper (7)

12 Seat of the faculty of reason (6)

15 Fluid in the mouth (6)

16 Utilising the energies of the sun (5)

18 Piece of cloth used for wiping the eyes or nose (abbr) (5)

20 Flip (a coin, for example) (4)

41

Across

1 Colour of the rainbow (6)
6 Peruser of text (6)
7 Cassette (4)
8 Stretchy fabric (7)
12 Cacophonous (5)
13 Unspecified (object) (3)
14 Disencumber (3)
15 Female sheep (3)
17 Force out of one's property (5)
18 Group which released *One Step Beyond* and *Night Boat to Cairo* (7)
21 Give forth (4)
22 Small rectangular block used in playing a game; the face of each having two equal areas bearing up to six dots each (6)
23 Court game (6)

Down

1 One behind the other (2,6)
2 Impoverished (8)
3 By word of mouth (4)
4 Flexible containers (4)
5 Plant exudation (5)
8 Nest of a bird of prey (5)
9 Assistants (5)
10 Lucky charm (8)
11 Urinary tract infection (8)
16 Wheeled, horse-drawn vehicle (5)
19 Carpentry pin (4)
20 Smut from a fire (4)

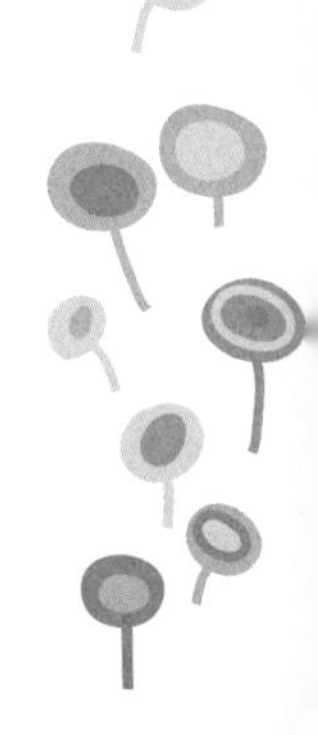

42

Across

1 Any of various small breeds of fowl (6)
6 Fleet of warships (6)
8 Public toilet in a military area (7)
9 Earnings (6)
10 Windstorm that lifts up clouds of dust (7)
13 Seventh letter of the Greek alphabet (3)
14 Be victorious (3)
17 Item commonly eaten on Shrove Tuesday (7)
20 Large North American deer (6)
21 Fabric made of silk (7)
22 Give up work (6)
23 Breed of monkey (6)

Down

1 Bundles, of straw or hay, for example (5)
2 Large brownish European flatfish (6)
3 Frenzied (5)
4 Singer married to Sean Penn from 1985–89 (7)
5 Frolic, cavort (5)
7 Fame, acclaim (6)
11 Abatement (7)
12 Jailor (6)
15 Glacial period (3,3)
16 Spin (5)
18 Clothes drier (5)
19 Chris ___, ex-husband of Billie Piper (5)

Across

1 Grilled bread (5)
4 Leonard Nimoy's character in *Star Trek* (5)
7 Protestant layman who assists the minister (6)
10 Hobble (4)
12 Displaying acceptance or certainty (8)
13 Asian spice (6)
14 Fluid-filled sac (4)
16 Preserve (4)
19 Oval-shaped nut (6)
22 Fabric (8)
23 Palm fruit (4)
24 Robert ___, actor who won an Oscar for *Raging Bull* (1980) (2,4)
25 Molars, for example (5)
26 Demands (5)

Down

1 News (7)
2 Adjust (5)
3 Relating to them (5)
5 Officer of the law (9)
6 Arrives (5)
8 Capable or efficient (9)
9 Skinflint (7)
11 Clinging plant (3)
15 Tiresome (7)
17 Astonish (5)
18 Charge levied on goods or services (inits) (3)
20 Long stay in bed in the morning (3-2)
21 Oily fruit (5)

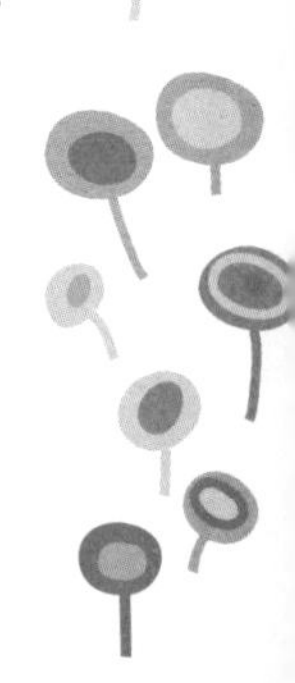

44

Across

1 Special way of doing something (5)
4 Rôle player (5)
7 Yarn that stands up from the weave (3)
8 Cowboy contest (5)
9 Sugar frosting (5)
10 Silvery metal (3)
11 Looks at (5)
14 Rapacity (5)
17 Acute insecurity (5)
20 Marsh plant (5)
23 Promissory note (inits) (3)
24 Acknowledge (5)
25 Trap for birds or small mammals (5)
26 Deciduous tree (3)
27 Sharp point on a plant (5)
28 Bay or cove (5)

Down

1 Russian city on the Vyatka River (5)
2 Mix up or confuse (5)
3 Tangles (5)
4 Caricaturing (5)
5 Clan (5)
6 Inflexible (5)
12 Tavern (3)
13 Used to be (3)
15 Cereal crop (3)
16 Hen's produce (3)
17 Expect (5)
18 Soup thickened with okra pods (5)
19 Mythological giant (5)
20 Japanese rice dish (5)
21 Slow speech pattern with prolonged vowels (5)
22 Select by a vote (5)

1		2		3	■	4	5		6	
	■		■		■	■		■		■
	■		■	7						
8			9		■	■		■		■
	■	■	10			11		■		■
12	13				■	14				15
■		■	16					■	■	
■		■		■	■	17		18		
19							■		■	
■		■		■	■		■		■	
20					■	21				

Across

1 Lads (5)

4 Augmenting (5)

7 Authoritative command (7)

8 Comedy characterised by improbable situations (5)

10 Bloodsucking insect parasitic on warm-blooded animals (5)

12 Synthetic fabric (5)

14 Characteristic of a city (5)

16 French river (5)

17 Plant exudation (5)

19 Italian composer remembered for his operas (1792–1868) (7)

20 Mooring (5)

21 Access (5)

Down

1 Bestow (6)

2 Slightly open (4)

3 Unspecified person (7)

5 Dish of rice, hard-boiled eggs and flaked fish (8)

6 Aquatic South American rodent resembling a small beaver (6)

9 Placed very near together (5-3)

11 Daybreak (7)

13 Niche (6)

15 Number written as XC in Roman numerals (6)

18 Gentle (4)

46

Across

1 Apply stiffening agent to cloth (6)

6 On the move (6)

7 Passage cut underground (6)

8 Chum (6)

10 Cruz Beckham's older brother (5)

13 Animal doctor (abbr) (3)

15 Wrongdoing (5)

18 Go on board (6)

20 Naval hero whose mistress was Lady Emma Hamilton (6)

21 Residential district, often run-down (6)

22 Heat (6)

Down

1 Forest god (5)

2 Use water to remove soap (5)

3 Fifty per cent (4)

4 Cocktail made of orange liqueur, lemon juice and brandy (7)

5 Prepared (5)

9 Customary observance (4)

11 Talked indistinctly (7)

12 Bowling period in the game of cricket (4)

14 Integrate (5)

16 Monarch (5)

17 Cattle farm (5)

19 Recognise (4)

47

Across

1 Weighing machine (6)
6 Wax drawing implement (6)
7 Light-sensitive membrane (6)
9 Wholly occupy (7)
10 Piece of metal held in a horse's mouth by reins (3)
12 Work actively for a political candidate or a party (11)
17 Woman's support garment (abbr) (3)
18 Abatement (7)
20 Connected to a computer network (6)
21 Daily news publications (6)
22 Covered with poorly groomed hair (6)

Down

1 Copyist (6)
2 Shrewd (6)
3 Examine hastily (4)
4 Head nurse (6)
5 Gun holder (7)
8 Bird's construction (4)
11 Against the law (7)
13 Secret code (6)
14 Kitchen appliance (4)
15 Flowing back or receding (6)
16 Not often (6)
19 Fling up (4)

48

Across

1 Tubes (5)
4 Roman god of love (5)
7 Aerial (7)
8 Youngest son of Tony Blair (3)
9 Check marks (5)
11 Because (5)
12 Blanches (5)
14 Scarper (5)
16 Dandy (3)
17 Jittery (7)
19 Unemotional person (5)
20 Public announcement of a proposed marriage (5)

Down

1 Building for carrying on industrial labour (5)
2 Cooking vessel (3)
3 Drops down (5)
4 Uncouth (5)
5 Pale lager with a strong flavour of hops (7)
6 Controlled a vehicle (5)
10 West Indian song (7)
12 Gasps (5)
13 Of sound (5)
14 Bush (5)
15 Old Testament prophet (5)
18 Have (3)

49

1		2		3	■	4		5		6
	■		■	7			■		■	
	■		■		■		■	8	9	
10										
	■	■	■		■		■	11		
■	12	13								■
14			■		■		■	■	■	15
16								17		
18			■		■		■		■	
	■		■	19			■		■	
20					■	21				

Across

1 Child's magazine (5)
4 Type of bread used as a pocket for filling (5)
7 Belonging to you and me (3)
8 Seaman (3)
10 Magic word used in a spell or in conjuring (11)
11 Of a thing (3)
12 Sends from one place to another (9)
14 Unit of gravitational force (3)
16 Feeling or manifesting veneration (11)
18 Yoko ___, widow of John Lennon (3)
19 Add up (3)
20 Military blockade (5)
21 Perpendicular (5)

Down

1 Clique (often secret) that seeks power usually through intrigue (5)
2 Heath (4)
3 Focus one's attention (11)
4 Have superior power and influence (11)
5 Choice morsel (6)
6 Tapestry used as a wall hanging (5)
9 Painting, sculpture, music, etc (4)
12 Adolescent (4)
13 Countermand (6)
14 One dozen dozen (5)
15 Treat with contemptuous disregard (5)
17 Lazy (4)

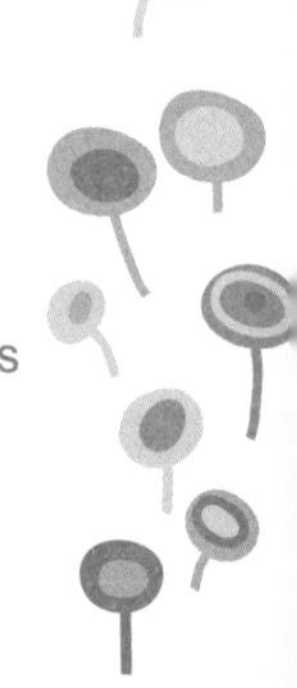

50

Across

1 Lacking flavour (9)
8 Anew (5)
9 Sketched (5)
10 Concert featuring bands (3)
11 Attitude, beliefs (5)
13 Follow as a result (5)
15 Beaks (5)
18 Chief monk (5)
20 Hand tool used to mark surfaces (3)
21 Welsh breed of dog (5)
22 Don a garment before purchase (3,2)
23 Ecstatic (9)

Down

2 Cause to be embarrassed (5)
3 Hinged lifting tool (5)
4 Gatehouse (5)
5 Crustlike surfaces of healing wounds (5)
6 Cheap novel (9)
7 Gut (9)
12 Nocturnal bird (3)
14 Bird's beak (3)
16 Immature insect (5)
17 Canonised person (5)
18 Communion table (5)
19 Slow-moving outlet of a lake (5)

51

1			2		3	■	■	4	■	5
	■	■		■	6	7				
8							■		■	
	■	■		■	9					
10		11		12			■		■	
■	■	13			■	14	15		■	■
16	■		■	17	18					19
20						■		■	■	
	■		■	21						
22						■		■	■	
	■		■	■	23					

Across

1 Silent movie star, ___ Swanson (1899–1983) (6)
6 Contusion (6)
8 Flat mass of frozen water floating at sea (3,4)
9 Narrow steep-sided valley (6)
10 Arid regions of the world (7)
13 Lyricist, ___ Gershwin (3)
14 Device used to propel a boat (3)
17 Solicit votes (7)
20 Stay away from deliberately (6)
21 Cocktail of vermouth and gin (7)
22 Sharp piercing cry (6)
23 Madden (6)

Down

1 Formal association of people with similar interests (5)
2 Roof-supporting beam (6)
3 Terminate before completion (5)
4 Coastal area between La Spezia in Italy and Cannes in France (7)
5 Sufferer from Hansen's disease (5)
7 Motive (6)
11 Heartfelt (7)
12 Elongated cluster of flowers (6)
15 Personification of a familiar idea (6)
16 Banquet (5)
18 Conscious, aware (5)
19 River that flows through Paris (5)

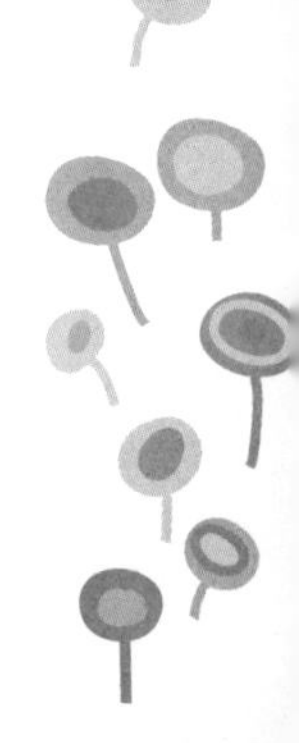

52

Across

1 Egyptian royal tomb (7)
7 Interior (5)
8 Communion plate (5)
9 Passage (7)
11 Less tainted (5)
13 Three-layered dragnet used for fishing (7)
17 Concern (5)
19 Retaliator (7)
22 Fool (5)
23 Hindu social class (5)
24 Perfumed (7)

Down

1 Unrequested internet browser window used for advertising (3-2)
2 Answer back (6)
3 Sacred word or syllable repeated in prayer (6)
4 Female operatic star (4)
5 Burden of responsibility (4)
6 Thin meat soup (5)
10 Yule (4)
12 ___ *Brockovich*, 2000 film starring Julia Roberts (4)
14 Maritime (6)
15 Lasso (6)
16 Impertinent (5)
18 In a softened tone (5)
20 Compass point (4)
21 Units of force associated with gravity (4)

53

1		2		3	■	4	5		6	
	■		■		■	■		■		■
	■		■	7						
8			9		■	■		■		■
	■	10			11			12		■
13	14			■		■	15			16
■	17					18			■	
■		■		■	■	19				
20							■		■	
■		■		■	■		■		■	
21					■	22				

Across

1 Coconut meat (5)
4 Work dough (5)
7 Take in too much food (7)
8 Supreme Teutonic god (5)
10 Albumen (3,5)
13 Adult male deer (4)
15 Drink often mixed with alcohol (4)
17 Startle (8)
19 Space set back or indented (5)
20 Ore (7)
21 Give tongue to (5)
22 Fritter away (5)

Down

1 Multitudes (6)
2 Flat highland (7)
3 In the middle of (5)
5 Spring flowers (8)
6 Astonished (6)
9 Infringe on the rights of, in law (8)
11 Period of conflict (3)
12 Protective shoe-coverings (7)
14 Close-fitting pullover or vest (1-5)
16 Strongly opposed, loath (6)
18 Relative by marriage (2-3)

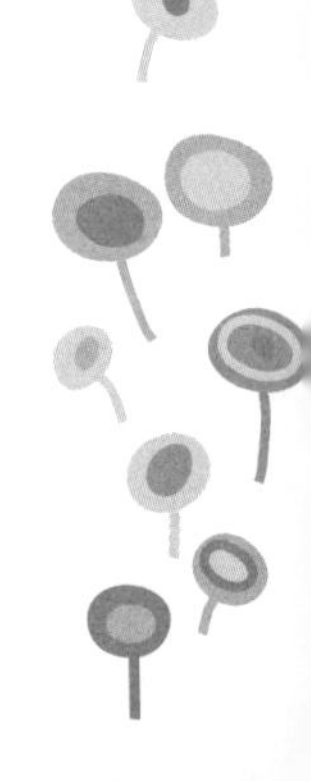

54

Across

4 Roman prophetess (5)
7 Underwater missile (7)
8 Column, of light for example (5)
10 Melodic subject of a musical composition (5)
12 Connect (3)
13 Guerilla (9)
17 Large vase (3)
19 Home planet (5)
22 Expiring (5)
23 Inclined to show mercy (7)
24 Cut of meat (5)

Down

1 Save up for future use (5)
2 Elaborately adorned (6)
3 Having more desirable qualities (6)
4 Type (4)
5 Uninteresting person (4)
6 Cloth woven from flax (5)
9 Foremost (5)
11 Hirsute (5)
14 Steering mechanism at the stern of a vessel (6)
15 Sharpshooter (6)
16 Shafts of light (5)
18 Semi-precious stone (5)
20 People who belong to the same genetic stock (4)
21 Mediocre and disdained writer (4)

1	2		3		■	4		5		6
■		■		■	7	■	■		■	
8				■	9					
	■	■	10			■	■		■	
11		12		■		■	13			
	■	14							■	
15				■		■	16			
	■		■	■	17			■	■	
18						■	19		20	
	■		■	■		■		■		■
21					■	22				

55

Across

1 Group of warships (5)
4 Metal conductors that carry electricity (5)
8 Nocturnal flightless bird of New Zealand (4)
9 Communion (6)
10 Large African antelope (3)
11 Room access (4)
13 Berth (4)
14 Replenishment (7)
15 Slow pace of running (4)
16 Culinary plant (4)
17 British dominion over India (3)
18 Capital of Austria (6)
19 Variety of agate (4)
21 Japanese dish (5)
22 Semi-precious stone with streaked colouring (5)

Down

2 Hawaiian wreath (3)
3 Woman who leaves one country to settle in another (7)
5 Meat cake (7)
6 Small shelter with an open front to protect a guardsman (6,3)
7 Piece of equipment used to catch small rodents (9)
8 Handle with ___, treat with extreme care (3,6)
12 Greek mythological musician, the husband of Eurydice (7)
13 Chinese tile game (3-4)
20 Nevertheless (3)

56

Across

1 Dealer in textiles (6)
6 Blossom (5)
7 Lubricant (3)
8 Glossy fabric (5)
10 Hostelry (3)
11 Wager (3)
13 Crazy (3)
14 Group that released the album *Twilight Of The Innocents* in 2007 (3)
16 Part of a curve (3)
17 Spring-loaded door fastener (5)
20 Entirely (3)
21 Grave robber (5)
22 Cross-breed (6)

Down

1 Creeping low plant (4)
2 Public violence (4)
3 Frugal (10)
4 ___ and Herzegovina, European country (6)
5 Unruffled (6)
6 Course of action that is unproductive (5,5)
9 Bladed chopping tool (3)
11 Hard ridge that forms the upper part of the nose (6)
12 Item used to brew a popular drink (6)
15 French word denoting that a wine is dry (3)
18 Excursion (4)
19 Manual worker (4)

57

Across

1 Detached (5)

4 Darken (3)

6 Spokes (5)

7 Excessively fat (5)

9 Adjusts a text ready for publication (5)

10 In any case (7)

13 Citadel of Moscow (7)

15 Wander (5)

16 Follow as a result (5)

17 Lacking experience of life (5)

18 Breed of dog originating in Asia (3)

19 Country, capital Madrid (5)

Down

1 Single-celled, water-living protozoon (6)

2 Released from confinement

3 Lines determining the limits of an area (5)

4 Heart stimulant derived from foxglove leaves (9)

5 Creeping low plant (4)

8 Catching in a trap (9)

11 Make a mistake (3)

12 Out of sight (6)

13 Ms Minogue (5)

14 Fencing swords (5)

15 Woman's sleeveless undergarment (4)

58

Across

3 Say out loud for the purpose of recording (7)
6 South American dance of African origin (5)
7 Region of northern Europe (7)
8 Divert in a specified direction (5)
10 Diminish (6)
12 Lowest adult male singing voice (4)
14 Fling (4)
17 Intrude in other people's affairs or business (6)
19 Britain's only native venomous snake (5)
20 Plans for attaining a particular goal (7)
21 Show appreciation (5)
22 Aseptic (7)

Down

1 Beetle considered divine by ancient Egyptians (6)
2 Cancels (6)
3 Valleys (5)
4 Endowed with natural abilities (8)
5 Court game (6)
9 Person who makes a will (8)
11 Total (3)
13 Appalled (6)
15 Difficult experience (6)
16 Refuse to work, as a protest (6)
18 Artificial gems (5)

59

Across

1 Make insensitive (6)

6 Of the eyes (6)

7 Cover in which a corpse is wrapped (6)

10 Outgrowth (9)

12 Send (payment) (5)

13 Girl's name (7)

16 Averse (5)

18 Plans and controls how a complex undertaking is done (9)

20 Most peculiar (6)

21 Lime tree (6)

22 Largest island in the Mediterranean (6)

Down

1 More lacking in honour or morality (5)

2 Ideal place (6)

3 Augur (4)

4 Unsure and constrained in manner (3,2,4)

5 Bottle that holds oil or vinegar for the table (5)

8 Acting violently, recklessly or destructively (9)

9 Improvement (6)

11 Pinned down (6)

14 Scandinavian (6)

15 Beautiful young woman (5)

17 With vehemence (5)

19 Long periods of time (4)

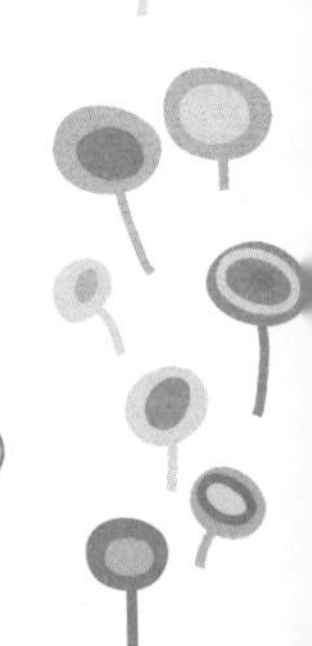

60

Across

1 Shop where hairdressers work (5)
3 Ill-tempered (5)
6 Get up (4)
8 Italian brandy made from the residue of grapes after pressing (6)
9 Tit for ___, getting even (3)
11 Russian pancake (5)
12 Twilled woollen fabric (5)
13 Common type of rodent (3)
14 Inhumane treatment (5)
15 Dodge (5)
18 Grandmother (3)
19 Glassy compound fused to the surface of an object for decoration (6)
20 Appear (4)
21 Level betting (5)
22 Brag (5)

Down

1 Scour vigorously (5)
2 Huge sea (5)
3 Baptise (8)
4 At a convenient or suitable time (9)
5 Empty area (5)
7 Specify as a condition or requirement (9)
10 With unflagging vitality (8)
14 Sharp, narrow ridge found in rugged mountains (5)
16 Lariat (5)
17 Insect such as an ant (5)

61

1		2			3	■	4	■	5	■
	■		■	■	6					
7				8		■		■		■
	■		■	9						
	■		■		■	■		■		■
10	11		12			13		14		15
■		■		■	■		■		■	
16					17		■		■	
■		■		■	18					
19						■	■		■	
■		■		■	20					

Across

1 Imperial capacity measure equal to four pecks (6)

6 Beefeater (6)

7 Water tanker (6)

9 Continue (7)

10 Guilty of betrayal or deception (11)

16 Capital of Kenya (7)

18 Call forth (6)

19 Musical composition of three or four movements of contrasting forms (6)

20 Fireball (6)

Down

1 Small lynx of North America (6)

2 Waste matter carried away in drains (6)

3 Harp used by Ancient Greeks (4)

4 Easier, less restricting (6)

5 Capital of the Bahamas (6)

8 Large-scale (4)

11 Rationality (6)

12 In a foreign country (6)

13 Extremely wicked (4)

14 Prophet (6)

15 Area, zone (6)

17 Shaft of light (4)

62

Across

1 Lose heat (4)
3 Bicycle seat (6)
5 Bustle (3)
6 Nautical term used in hailing (4)
7 Foolish (6)
9 All (10)
14 Fixed conventionalised or stock image (10)
17 Fast gait of a horse (6)
19 Go off, as with milk (4)
20 ___ *Maria*, prayer to the Virgin Mary (3)
21 Loveliness (6)
22 Tatters (4)

Down

1 Swiss cottage (6)
2 Stratum (5)
3 Call for help (inits) (3)
4 Mendacious (5)
8 Mr Geller, spoon-bender (3)
10 Young newt (3)
11 Be equal, draw (3)
12 Word indicating a negative answer (3)
13 One of four playing-card suits (6)
14 Frighten away (5)
15 Long and slippery fish (3)
16 Weapon that delivers a temporarily paralysing electric shock (5)
18 Hand over money (3)

63

1			2			3	4			5
					6					
7		8					9			
10					11			12		
										13
	14		15				16			
17										
18					19		20			
21						22				

Across

1 Frown (5)
3 Bottomless gulf (5)
7 Fanciful but graceful asymmetric ornamentation (6)
9 Horse's coat when sprinkled with white or grey (4)
10 Acute discomfort (4)
11 Fees levied for the use of roads (5)
14 Country comprising a group of islands, capital Apia (5)
16 ___ Armstrong, first man on the moon (4)
18 Elderly (4)
19 Disease transmitted by body lice (6)
21 Highland Games pole (5)
22 Accolade (5)

Down

1 Actor's lines (6)
2 Romance (3)
4 Coloured transparent gemstone (5)
5 Despatched (4)
6 As fast as possible (4-5)
8 Crockery (5)
12 Bloodsucking parasite (5)
13 Shut (6)
15 Small biting fly (5)
17 Bath powder (4)
20 Church bench (3)

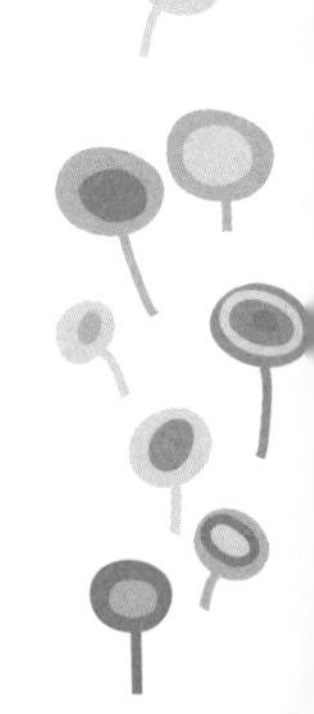

64

Across

1 Frolic, cavort (5)
4 Framework of a military unit (5)
7 Passes along (6)
9 Long narrative poem (4)
10 At the summit of (4)
11 Hun king nicknamed the 'Scourge of God' (6)
13 Archaic form of the word 'you' (4)
15 Distinctive and stylish elegance (4)
17 Open, a bottle of wine for example (6)
20 Halo of light (4)
21 Travelling show (4)
22 Hold in high regard (6)
23 Popular board game (5)
24 Bent from a vertical position (5)

Down

1 Butchery (7)
2 Aviator (5)
3 Kingly (5)
5 Sterile (7)
6 Powerful herbivore with a horned snout (abbr) (5)
8 Natural height of a person (7)
12 Entrails (7)
14 Not properly maintained, slovenly (7)
16 Chain used to restrain an animal (5)
18 Relating to the organ of smell (5)
19 Drama that is sung (5)

65

1			2	■	3	4			5	
	■	■	6				■	■		■
7				■	8					
	■	■		■	■		■	■		■
9		10			11			12		■
	■		■	■		■	■		■	13
■	14			15			16			
■		■	■		■	■		■	■	
17					18	■	19			
■		■	■	20				■	■	
21						■	22			

Across

1 Oil reservoir in an engine (4)
3 Knit hose covering the body from the waist to the feet (6)
6 Compound capable of turning litmus red (4)
7 River that flows through Bristol (4)
8 Sign of the zodiac (6)
9 Sheet of slate, for writing with chalk (10)
14 Go against, as of rules and laws (10)
17 Disappear from view (6)
19 Headlong plunge into water (4)
20 Equipment for a horse (4)
21 Forever (6)
22 Confederate, accomplice (4)

Down

1 Tattered (6)
2 Be overcome by a sudden fear (5)
3 Nervous twitch (3)
4 US state, capital Boise (5)
5 Popular taste at a given time (5)
10 Gone by (3)
11 Rigid piece of metal (3)
12 Strong-scented perennial herb (3)
13 Solution or cure (6)
14 Move on hands and knees (5)
15 Delicious (5)
16 Hard drink originating in Russia (5)
18 Owns (3)

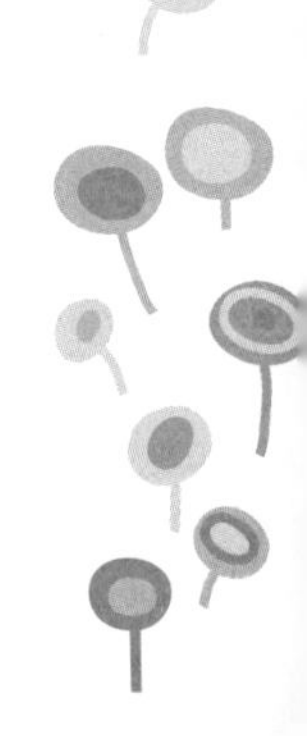

66

Across

1 Reddish-brown tint (5)
4 Venomous snake (5)
7 Large basket (usually one of a pair) carried by a beast of burden (7)
8 *Much ___ About Nothing*, Shakespeare play (3)
9 Inventories (5)
11 Fried quickly in a little fat (5)
12 Media personality, ___ Street-Porter (5)
14 Fill quickly beyond capacity (5)
16 Chinese communist leader (1893–1976) (3)
17 Acts in a threatening manner (7)
19 Expels (5)
20 Assortment (5)

Down

1 Floral leaf (5)
2 Writing implement (3)
3 Haywire (5)
4 Coagulated milk used to make cheese (5)
5 Brilliant and showy technical skill (7)
6 Got up (5)
10 Curving in and out (7)
12 Elephantine (5)
13 Multiplication (5)
14 Echo sounder (acronym) (5)
15 Temporary police force (5)
18 Metal container (3)

67

1			2			3		4		5
6						7				
8	9			10				11	12	
13		14		15			16			17
18						19				
20						21				

Across

1 Restores to working order (5)
3 Strange (5)
6 Upstanding or highborn (5)
7 Prod (5)
8 Fulfil requirements (7)
11 Mature (3)
13 Liveliness and energy (3)
15 Certify (7)
18 Perform without preparation (2-3)
19 Cuts into pieces (5)
20 Eye with malicious satisfaction (5)
21 Shrimp-like planktonic crustaceans (5)

Down

1 Subtraction (5)
2 City in 4 Down (5)
3 Vexed (7)
4 Asian country (5)
5 Female relative (5)
9 Overwhelming feeling of wonder (3)
10 Fizzy, sugary powder (7)
12 Hydrogen, for instance (3)
13 Car crash (sl) (5)
14 Acute viral disease (5)
16 Different (5)
17 Display stand for a painting (5)

68

Across

1 Layer of ground containing a mat of grass and grass roots (4)
3 Bulb, traditionally from Holland (5)
6 Napoleon's exile island (4)
7 Highway (4)
9 Soliloquy (9)
11 Iraq's second largest city (5)
12 Point of a joke (3,4)
15 Blue ___, flag indicating a ship is ready to sail (5)
17 Piece of paper recording tasks planned or done on a project (9)
18 Unable to hear (4)
19 Murder (4)
20 Two-syllable feet in poetry (5)
21 White-tailed sea eagle (4)

Down

1 Pound, pulse (5)
2 Hat made of felt with a creased crown (6)
3 Car exhaust (8)
4 Pair of spectacles on a long handle (9)
5 More lacking in colour (5)
8 Constitutional capital of The Netherlands (9)
10 City in southern Japan on Kyushu (8)
13 Knitting tool (6)
14 Hindu religious teacher (5)
16 Type of firearm (5)

69

1			2	3	■	4	■	5		6
	■	■	7						■	
8		9			■		■		■	
	■		■	10	11					
12						■	■		■	■
	■		■	13		14	■		■	15
■	■		■	■	16					
17				18			■		■	
	■		■		■	19	20			
	■	21						■	■	
22			■		■	23				

Across

1 Detector used to locate distant objects (5)
5 Long and slippery fish (3)
7 Sour-tasting yellow fruits (6)
8 One more time (5)
10 Scottish bread (7)
12 Cream-filled pastry (6)
13 Propel with oars (3)
16 Comfort, solace (6)
17 Author of *The Canterbury Tales* (7)
19 Asian peninsula separating the Yellow Sea and the East Sea (5)
21 Spider's snare (6)
22 Shade, tinge (3)
23 Narrow raised strip (5)

Down

1 Harvested (6)
2 Muhammad ___, former boxer (3)
3 Auguste ___, French impressionist painter (1841–1919) (6)
4 Vessel for travel on water (4)
5 Moving staircase (9)
6 Delicate, woven and decorative fabric (4)
9 Leeway (9)
11 Sprang up (5)
14 Employee (6)
15 Period of ten years (6)
17 Ready money (4)
18 Three-dimensional shape (4)
20 Kimono sash (3)

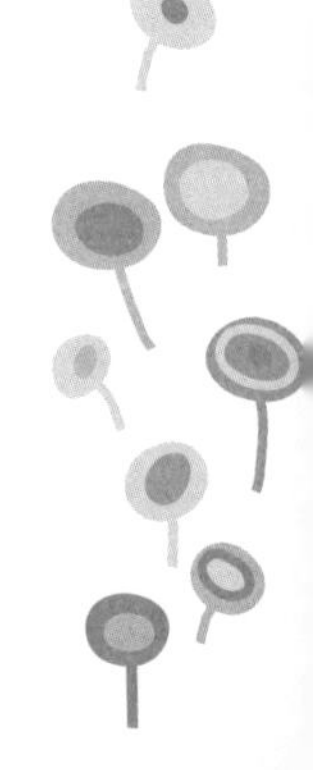

70

Across

1 Firework that burns with a fizzing noise (5)

4 Become rotten, as of an egg, for example (5)

7 Playfully mischievous child, rascal (9)

9 Chuck (5)

10 Single level of a building (5)

12 Ridge of rock, coral, etc (4)

14 British nobleman (4)

16 In addition (5)

18 Containing nothing (5)

20 Small thin sausage (9)

21 Sir Thomas ___, English poet (1503–42) (5)

22 Long (for) (5)

Down

1 Area, zone (6)

2 Former communist country (inits) (4)

3 Noisy altercation (5)

5 Had musings or fantasies while awake (9)

6 Person who inspires others (6)

8 Tall receptacle in which a popular drink is brewed (6,3)

11 Known (3)

13 Number signified by the Roman LXXX (6)

15 Non-professional person (6)

17 Prepared for action (5)

19 Daddy (4)

71

1		2		3	■	4		5		6
	■		■	7			■		■	
8			9		■		■	10		
	■	■	11				■		■	
12	13				■	14	15		16	
■		■		■	■	■		■		■
17		18		19	■	20				21
	■		■	22				■	■	
23			■		■	24		25		
	■		■	26			■		■	
27					■	28				

Across

1 Barrage (5)
4 Will (5)
7 Dignitary (inits) (3)
8 Adult insect (5)
10 Shoddy or tasteless articles (3)
11 Rivulet (4)
12 Flowed back (5)
14 Above average in size (5)
17 Asian peninsula (5)
20 Chafe at the bit, like a horse (5)
22 Alone (4)
23 Spherical object (3)
24 Very angry (5)
26 Important timber tree (3)
27 Dead language (5)
28 Washtubs (5)

Down

1 Steeple (5)
2 Grazing land (3)
3 Egg-shaped object (5)
4 Piece of rolled paper used to light a fire (5)
5 Communion table (5)
6 Underworld river (5)
9 Small compact-bodied almost completely aquatic bird (5)
13 Hoot with derision (3)
15 Detest (5)
16 Place to work out (3)
17 Small natural hill (5)
18 Prove to be false (5)
19 Poplar tree (5)
20 Ascend (5)
21 Squeeze (5)
25 Represent (3)

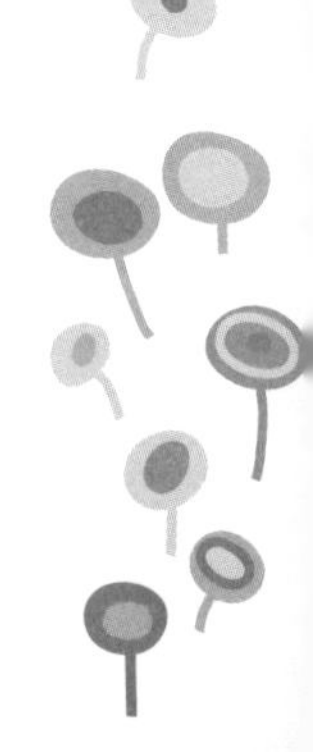

72

Across

1 Committee (5)

3 Ecstasy (5)

6 Plant family which includes the maple (4)

8 Person held in servitude (5)

9 Sensations of acute discomfort (5)

10 Make changes in text (4)

11 Resin used in laminates (5)

13 Custodian of a museum (7)

15 Foam or froth on the sea (5)

16 Mountain lake (4)

18 Measure of the weight of a gemstone (5)

19 Domestic birds (5)

20 Rear (4)

21 North African port (5)

22 Facial hair (5)

Down

1 Freedom from disputes (5)

2 Printed mistake (7)

3 Smooth-haired breed of hound (6)

4 Italian word for a woman loved or loving (9)

5 Sleazy or shabby (5)

7 Displaying luxury and furnishing gratification to the senses (9)

12 Suitable for drinking (7)

14 Area set back or indented (6)

15 Instance of visual perception (5)

17 Bare (5)

73

1	■	2	■	3	■	4		5		6
7							■		■	
	■		■		■		■		■	
8			9		■	10	11			
	■	12			■	■		■	■	
■	13					14		15		■
16	■	■		■	■	17			■	18
19		20		21	■	22				
	■		■		■		■		■	
	■		■	23						
24					■		■		■	

Across

4 Bad-tempered expression (5)
7 Underwater missile (7)
8 Leave or strike out, as of vowels (5)
10 Out of fashion (5)
12 Immoral act (3)
13 Optical instrument used in a submarine (9)
17 Expression of surprise or of sudden comprehension (3)
19 Daisy-like flower (5)
22 Strong, lightweight wood (5)
23 Daybreak (7)
24 Postpone (5)

Down

1 Warhorse (5)
2 Ocean trip taken for pleasure (6)
3 Native of Sana'a, for example (6)
4 Dish often served as a first course (4)
5 Rowing poles (4)
6 Identification tab (5)
9 Hymn of mourning (5)
11 Hawaiian greeting (5)
14 Small rooms on a ship (6)
15 Abnormally deficient in colour (6)
16 Rolled up, as with straw or hay (5)
18 Ring-shaped bread roll (5)
20 High in stature (4)
21 Pink-tinged (4)

74

Across

1 Retail establishments (5)
3 Damp (5)
6 Ancient Peruvian (4)
8 Large shrimps often coated in batter (6)
9 Tune (3)
11 Style or category of art, music or literature (5)
12 French composer of works such as Boléro (5)
14 Certificate awarded by an educational establishment (7)
15 More glacial (5)
16 Wealthy man (5)
18 Unwell (3)
19 Rhododendron-like shrub (6)
20 Cogwheel (4)
21 Greek island (5)
22 Have a cigarette (5)

Down

1 Scarf bandage (5)
2 Grassy plain (7)
3 Pasta in the form of slender tubes (8)
4 Not possible to shift (9)
5 Experiment (5)
7 Nominee (9)
10 Stay of execution (8)
13 Dental filler (7)
15 ___ Asimov, science-fiction writer (5)
17 Capital of Switzerland (5)

75

1		2			3	■	4	■	5	■
	■		■	■	6					
7				■		■		■		■
	■		■	8		9		10		11
12					■		■	13		
	■		■	14			■		■	
15	16		■		■	17				
18			19		20		■		■	
■		■		■		■	21			
22						■	■		■	
■		■		■	23					

Across

1 Trousers for casual wear (6)
6 Medicated lozenge used to soothe the throat (6)
7 Capital of the former West Germany (4)
8 Back, patronise (7)
12 Brightly-coloured tropical freshwater fishes (5)
13 Expend (3)
14 Word expressing disgust (3)
15 Acquired (3)
17 Fasten by passing rope through a hole (5)
18 Christian recluse (7)
21 Tells trivial lies (4)
22 Island in French Polynesia, capital Papeete (6)
23 Form of a word used to denote more than one (6)

Down

1 Deliberate act of destruction or disruption (8)
2 Supply with critical comments (8)
3 Footprint (4)
4 Substantive word (4)
5 Pandemonium (5)
8 Of an Arabic royal family (5)
9 Clay pigment (5)
10 Deepest of the Great Lakes (8)
11 Turnaround (8)
16 Group of tissues performing a function (5)
19 Female domestic (4)
20 Journey (4)

76

Across

3 Stop the flow of a liquid (7)
6 Cook in a simmering liquid (5)
7 Manifest, plain (7)
8 Harden to (5)
10 Breadwinner (6)
12 Soap froth (4)
14 Edible fat (4)
17 Nazi dictator during World War II (6)
19 Racing vessel (5)
20 Person who has been given the freedom of a city or borough (7)
21 Capital of Egypt (5)
22 Awaited king of the Jews (7)

Down

1 Physical science relating to light (6)
2 Appreciated (6)
3 Downright (5)
4 Beneath the surface of the ocean (8)
5 Savoury appetiser (6)
9 Impetuosity (8)
11 Mesh (3)
13 False (6)
15 Scruffy child (6)
16 Design marked onto the skin (6)
18 Kill without legal sanction (5)

77

1		2		3	■	4	5		6	
	■		■		■	■		■		■
	■	7	8		9					
10						■		■		■
	■	■	11					■		■
12	13			■		■	14			15
■		■	16			17		■	■	
■		■		■	18			19		
20									■	
■		■		■	■		■		■	
21					■	22				

Across

1 Bulgarian capital (5)
4 Country, capital Cairo (5)
7 Having a striking or revealing effect (9)
10 Plant similar to the rhododendron (6)
11 Finely powdered tobacco (5)
12 Fabric interwoven with threads of metal (4)
14 Speech defect (4)
16 Chock (5)
18 Enclose in (6)
20 Make merry (9)
21 Mechanical bar (5)
22 Coating (5)

Down

1 Lie with one's limbs spread out (6)
2 Type of Greek cheese (4)
3 Dave ___, Irish comedian who died in 2005 (5)
5 Bend the knees and bow in church (9)
6 Structure supporting the lower limbs (6)
8 In another location (9)
9 Wash clothes (7)
13 Unit of electric current (6)
15 Like better (6)
17 Twist into a state of deformity (5)
19 Light and insubstantial (poetic) (4)

78

Across

1 Piece of cloth used to mend a hole (5)
3 Evoking lifelike images within the mind (5)
6 Prior to a specified time (7)
8 Definite article (3)
9 Facilitate (4)
10 Allowing (7)
13 Barrier that contains the flow of water (3)
15 Come into (5)
17 Small ocean (3)
19 Caller (7)
21 Carries out (4)
22 Curious (3)
23 Analysed (7)
24 Outer surfaces of an object (5)
25 Interlace (5)

Down

1 Milky-white gem (5)
2 Bring into existence (6)
3 Long journeys (7)
4 Took part in a ballot (5)
5 Reverie (5)
7 Odontologist (7)
11 Organ of sight (3)
12 Lays out money for profit, as by buying shares, etc (7)
14 In the past (3)
16 Verbal puzzle (6)
17 Items of footwear (5)
18 Contributed (5)
20 Long, narrow hill (5)

79

Across

1 Sudden intense sensation or emotion (6)
6 Takes control of (without authority and possibly with force) (6)
7 Argentine plain (6)
9 Frame supporting the body of a car (7)
13 Sceptic (5)
14 Bike (5)
15 Natives of Bern, for example (5)
18 Man-eating giants (5)
19 Tokens used for admission, travel, etc (7)
21 Have a lofty goal (6)
22 Tyre accessories that increase traction (6)
23 Edible part of a nut (6)

Down

1 Associated with a particular rôle or character (8)
2 Amorous (8)
3 Growing in extreme abundance (4)
4 Finicky (5)
5 Month with 30 days (5)
8 Level a charge against (6)
10 To the opposite side (6)
11 Arachnid with a sting in the tail (8)
12 Outer casing of a marine organism (8)
16 Isle and county in southern England (5)
17 Coil of knitting wool (5)
20 Errand (4)

80

Across

1 Devout (5)
4 Dried flowers used in brewing (4)
6 Polynesian rain dance (4)
7 Garden tool (4)
8 Emergency care (5,3)
12 Filter (4)
14 Cocktail fruit (5)
15 Fungus producing black spores, that affects plants (4)
16 Fervent supporter of a person or institution (8)
20 Offshore area (4)
21 A few (4)
22 Lower limbs (4)
23 Public dance hall (5)

Down

1 Light gust of air (4)
2 Above, beyond (4)
3 Fired a bullet (4)
4 Forceful and insistent advertising (4,4)
5 Cleaned with a broom (5)
9 Individual unit (4)
10 Immaculate (8)
11 Cordiality (5)
13 Sudden uncontrollable attacks (4)
15 Cause to flow out or over (5)
17 In one's sleeping place (4)
18 Wading bird with a long, slender, down-curved bill (4)
19 Country, capital Lomé (4)

1	2		3		■	4		5		6
■		■		■	7	■	■		■	
8				■	9					
	■	■	10	11		■	■		■	
12		13				■	14			
	■	15				16			■	
17				■	18					
	■		■	■	19			■	■	
20						■	21		22	
	■		■	■		■		■		■
23					■	24				

Across

1 Temporary love of an adolescent (5)
4 One of a series published periodically (5)
8 Funeral pile (4)
9 Straying from the right course (6)
10 Hour at which something is due (inits) (3)
12 Endured (6)
14 Face (4)
15 Charming in a childlike or naive way (7)
17 Woody plant (4)
18 One dozen (6)
19 Completely (3)
20 Swimmer (6)
21 Salver (4)
23 Foxhole (5)
24 Inebriated (5)

Down

2 Column of light (3)
3 Term of endearment (7)
5 Sporting dog (7)
6 To a high degree (9)
7 Advantage gained by beginning early (as in a race) (4,5)
8 Acceptable to the taste (9)
11 Cardinal number (3)
13 Knitted jumper (7)
14 Industrial plant for extracting metal from ore (7)
16 Nocturnal bird (3)
22 Beard found on a bract of grass (3)

82

Across

1 Ocean floor (6)

6 Dictates (6)

7 Thin layers of rock used for roofing (6)

8 Refuse to work, as a protest (6)

10 Fails to win (5)

13 Crush by treading heavily (7)

16 Artist's tripod (5)

18 Borne on the water (6)

20 Cipher used by Germany during World War II (6)

21 Speaker (6)

22 Muslim place of worship (6)

Down

1 Fibre used for making rope (5)

2 Annoy (6)

3 Sleep in a convenient place (4)

4 Makes up one's mind (7)

5 Eastern county (5)

9 Use a keyboard (4)

11 Emanating from stars (7)

12 Epic tale (4)

14 Women (6)

15 Civic leader (5)

17 Depart, go (5)

19 School period (4)

83

Across

1 Swimmer (6)
4 Second letter of the Greek alphabet (4)
6 Loss of the ability to move a body part (9)
8 ___ Mahler, composer, 1860–1911 (6)
12 Leer (4)
13 Live (5)
15 Norse deity (4)
16 Writer (6)
19 Obsess (9)
20 Artificial hairpieces (4)
21 Act against an attack (6)

Down

1 Slang term for ostentatious jewellery (5)
2 Strings (5)
3 Soft yellow substance secreted by aural glands (6)
4 Refuse to do business with (7)
5 Pompous fool (3)
7 Inuit dwelling (5)
9 Mammary gland of bovids (5)
10 Flimsy (7)
11 Through (3)
14 Surgical stitch (6)
17 Sir Fred ___, English astrophysicist (1915–2001) (5)
18 Ball-shaped (5)
19 Animal's foot (3)

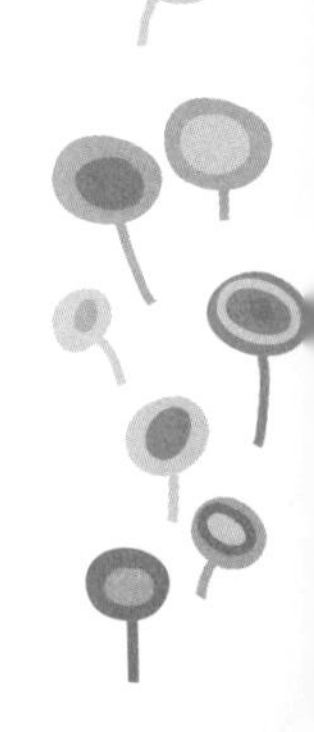

84

Across

1 Cricketing trophy (5)
4 Greta ___, film star (1905–90) (5)
7 Annual publication giving weather forecasts, etc (7)
8 Deep yellow colour (5)
9 Cavalryman (7)
13 City, site of the Taj Mahal (4)
16 Bulge or swelling (4)
17 Music with a syncopated melody (7)
19 Church passage (5)
20 Continuous (7)
21 Carrying weapons (5)
22 Adjust again after an initial failure (5)

Down

1 Spanish fortress or palace built by the Moors (7)
2 City in Germany on the Elbe River (7)
3 Commence (5)
5 Major river of Brazil (6)
6 Favouring one person or side over another (6)
10 Male sheep (3)
11 Have (7)
12 Acknowledgment that payment has been made (7)
14 Gather, as of crops (6)
15 In one's place of residence (2,4)
18 Enthusiastic (5)

85

1	■	2		3		4		5		
	■		■		■		■		■	■
6			7		■	8	9			10
	■	11							■	
12					■	13				
	■	■		■	■	■		■	■	
14		15		16	■	17		18		
	■	19							■	
20					■	21				
■	■		■		■		■		■	
22									■	

Across

2 Trait of lacking courage (9)
6 Bring dishonour upon (5)
8 Iridescent internal layer of a mollusc shell (5)
11 Discolour, usually with use or wear (7)
12 *A Town like ___*, Nevil Shute novel (5)
13 Painful eyelid swellings (5)
14 Perfect type (5)
17 Fruit pulp (5)
19 Suppose (7)
20 Hand tool for boring holes (5)
21 Derive, evoke (5)
22 Private conversation between two people (4-1-4)

Down

1 Republic in Central America (5,4)
2 American raccoon (5)
3 In what place? (5)
4 Hindu queens (5)
5 Deserving of a scratch (5)
7 Relatively coarse lace made by weaving and knotting cords (7)
9 Bedazzle with wonder (7)
10 Ovoid chocolate treat associated with a spring festival (6,3)
15 Number (5)
16 Immature insect (5)
17 Fragment (5)
18 Put back into service after processing (5)

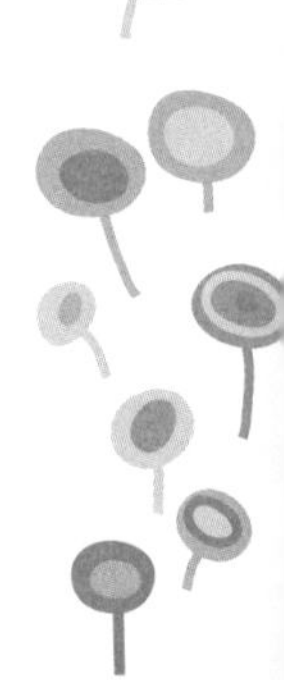

86

Across

1 Milk-pudding ingredient (4)
3 Toy figures (5)
6 Live-action film about a piglet (4)
7 Fully developed (4)
9 Not good (3)
10 Ugly object (7)
12 Distant but within sight (poetical) (3)
13 Cane spirit (3)
14 Nationalist (7)
15 ___ de Cologne, perfume (3)
16 ___ and outs, details (3)
18 Ireland's longest river (7)
20 First note in the tonic sol-fa scale (3)
21 Monetary unit of Uruguay (4)
22 Stead (4)
23 Thin strands of metal (5)
24 Gentle, indulgent (4)

Down

1 Regretful (5)
2 Conform (4)
3 Commitment to some purpose (8)
4 Man who is morally unrestrained (9)
5 Biblical city (5)
8 Clerk who does boring, repetitive paperwork (3-6)
11 Internal organs, collectively (8)
15 Give qualities or abilities to (5)
17 Pig's nose (5)
19 Musical composition (4)

87

Across

2 Entrance used by theatre personnel (5,4)
6 Spokes (5)
7 Giraffe-like creature (5)
9 Diving bird of northern seas (3)
10 John ___, pioneering US astronaut (5)
12 Small heron (5)
14 Declares or affirms as true (5)
17 Sun-dried brick (5)
19 The type of wind that blows no good (3)
20 Despised (5)
21 Board used with a planchette (5)
22 Employee who mixes and serves alcoholic drinks (9)

Down

1 Section of writing (9)
2 Grasslike marsh plant (5)
3 Relating to birds (5)
4 Call forth (5)
5 Transmitting live (2-3)
8 Lacking information (2,3,4)
11 Immediately (3)
13 Wander aimlessly in search of pleasure (3)
15 Further from the centre (5)
16 Move furtively (5)
17 Not silently (5)
18 Flexible twig of a willow tree (5)

88

Across

- **1** Five-stringed instrument (5)
- **4** Cooked in an oven (5)
- **7** Mimi ___, Tom Cruise's first wife (6)
- **9** Factual (4)
- **10** Pinnacle (4)
- **12** Hoop that covers a wheel (4)
- **13** Steed (5)
- **15** Steal from a person (3)
- **17** Part of a collar (5)
- **19** Exchange for money (4)
- **21** Biblical first man (4)
- **23** Bicycle accessory (4)
- **24** Duty list (6)
- **25** Brings up (5)
- **26** Loose-fitting garment (5)

Down

- **1** Censure severely or angrily (6)
- **2** African country, capital Abuja (7)
- **3** Vegetable known as lady's fingers (4)
- **5** Later than (5)
- **6** Sketched (4)
- **8** Learned person (7)
- **11** Disorderly crowd of people (3)
- **14** Add sugar (7)
- **15** Scarlet (3)
- **16** Priest or religious leader (6)
- **18** Writing material (5)
- **20** Goad (4)
- **22** Debatable (4)

89

1	■	2	■	3			4		5	
6					■	■		■		■
	■		■	7						
8					■	■		■		■
	■		■	9	10			11		12
13	14		15	■		■	16			
17						18	■		■	
■		■		■	■	19				
20							■		■	
■		■		■	■	21				
22							■		■	

Across

3 Perched (7)
6 Asp, for example (5)
7 Deluge (7)
8 ___ Wilde, dramatist (5)
9 Action of attacking an enemy (7)
13 Thought (4)
16 Cosmetic preparation used to darken the edges of the eyelids (4)
17 Female siblings (7)
19 Area of the body below the ribs (5)
20 Cosa Nostra members (7)
21 Words used to refer to people, places or objects (5)
22 Arsonist (7)

Down

1 Diffusion of liquid through a porous membrane (7)
2 Captures in the hands (7)
3 Reminiscent of the past (fashion) (5)
4 Sharp piercing cry (6)
5 Harem guard (6)
10 In favour of (3)
11 Injurious to health (7)
12 One who believes in rule by a select group (7)
14 Hindu Festival of Lights (6)
15 Clothing (6)
18 Plaything that moves back and forth (5)

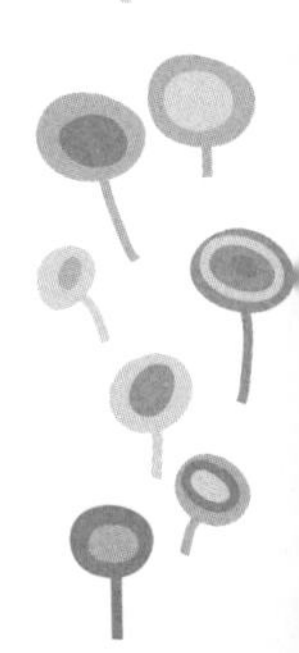

90

1			2		■	3		4		5
	■	■		■	■		■		■	
6									■	
	■	■		■	■		■		■	
7		8		■	9					
■	■		■	10			■		■	■
11						■	12			13
	■		■		■	■		■	■	
	■	14								
	■		■		■	■		■	■	
15					■	16				

Across

1 Articulation (5)

3 Grinds (5)

6 Reference points against which other things can be evaluated (9)

7 Part of an animal (4)

9 Arm joints (6)

10 Unspecified (object or degree) (3)

11 Amigo (6)

12 Region regularly afflicted by monsoons (4)

14 Copiousness (9)

15 Carapace (5)

16 Brute (5)

Down

1 Go to see (5)

2 Long, narrow strip of water (5)

3 Only, just (6)

4 Morals, examples (7)

5 Reveals (5)

8 Copy (7)

9 Put a stop to (3)

10 Yearly (6)

11 Confronts bravely (5)

12 Cognisant (5)

13 Broker (5)

91

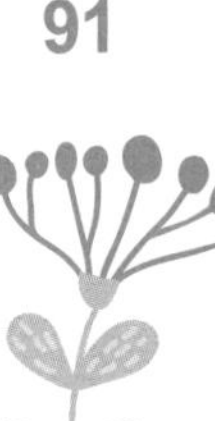

Across

1 Obvious and dull (5)
3 Firm open-weave fabric used by window-cleaners (5)
7 Positive or favourable aspect (6)
10 Young horse (4)
11 The smallest quantity (4)
12 Type of craftsman (10)
15 Type of coffee topped with steamed milk and milk froth (10)
20 In a fresh way (4)
21 Archaic word meaning 'in the direction of' (4)
22 Thin top layer on a solid floor (6)
23 Curl of the lip (5)
24 Climbing plant supporter (5)

Down

1 Injury that discolours the skin (6)
2 Person born under the sign of the ram (5)
4 Turned-back hems at the ends of sleeves (5)
5 Dairy product (4)
6 Pay back (9)
8 Fixture found on a chimney stack (3)
9 Epidermal pore in a leaf or stem (5)
13 Characteristic of a sheep (5)
14 Solid substance in the form of tiny loose particles (6)
16 Dig into (5)
17 Freight (5)
18 Maiden name indicator (3)
19 Informal name for a cat (4)

92

Across

1 Medicine that induces vomiting (6)

6 Annie ___, famous US sharpshooter (6)

8 Swimmers (7)

9 Absorb food (6)

10 Demise (5)

13 Local idiom (7)

16 Acute (5)

18 Steam baths (6)

20 Earmark (7)

21 Order of business (6)

22 Tenant (6)

Down

1 Implant (5)

2 Island in French Polynesia, capital Papeete (6)

3 Rope (4)

4 Canadian province (7)

5 Abnormal swellings on the body (5)

7 Lines directed to an audience (6)

11 Urged solemnly or earnestly (7)

12 Source of danger (6)

14 Shouts of approval (6)

15 Commonly encountered (5)

17 Fragment (5)

19 Marine mammal (4)

93

Across

1 Small portable timepiece (5)
4 Coherent (5)
8 Thaw (4)
9 Be preoccupied with something (6)
10 Forest tree (3)
12 Edict (6)
14 Foodstuff grown in paddy-fields (4)
15 Dreadful (7)
17 Bellow (4)
18 Fleshy underground stems or roots (6)
19 Had a meal (3)
20 Cargo ship designed to carry crude oil in bulk (6)
21 Heavy metal (4)
23 Reigns over (5)
24 Breakfast rasher (5)

Down

2 Chopping tool (3)
3 Food provider (7)
5 Woman's sleeveless undergarment (7)
6 Distributed or weighted out in carefully determined portions (9)
7 Brief (9)
8 One who presides over a forum or debate (9)
11 Hawaiian garland of flowers (3)
13 Canal (7)
14 Contagious viral disease, a form of measles (7)
16 Known (3)
22 Rapid bustling commotion (3)

94

Across

1 Tailed heavenly body (5)
3 Birds' bills (5)
7 Steal cattle (6)
9 Endorsement made in a passport (4)
10 Golf peg (3)
12 Cousin's mother (4)
13 Mouth-watering (5)
15 For every (3)
17 Flexible twig of a willow tree (5)
19 Celestial body (4)
21 Former Chinese leader (3)
22 Shade of blue tinged with green (4)
23 Of or relating to cats (6)
25 River that flows through Kelso (5)
26 Financial institutions (5)

Down

1 Marked by the appetites and passions of the body (6)
2 Consume food (3)
4 Fairies that are somewhat mischievous (5)
5 Piece of cotton used to apply medication (4)
6 In a more fortunate or prosperous condition (6,3)
8 Air cavity in the skull (5)
11 Head of corn (3)
14 For all (music) (5)
15 Green vegetable (3)
16 Tight-fitting underpants (6)
18 Likeness (5)
20 Sturdy upright pole (4)
24 Field covered with grass (3)

95

1		2		3	■	4	5		6	
	■		■		■	■		■		■
	■		■	7						
8					■	■		■		■
	■		■	9	10			11		12
13	14		15	■		■	16			
17						18	■		■	
■		■		■	■	19				
20							■		■	
■		■		■	■		■		■	
21					■	22				

Across

1 Acute (5)
4 Pale (5)
7 In a little while (7)
8 Part of the leg between the hip and the knee (5)
9 Alongside each other (7)
13 Make changes in text (4)
16 Toy flown in the wind (4)
17 Equivalent word (7)
19 Dined at home (3,2)
20 Frankness (7)
21 One stroke over par in golf (5)
22 For this reason (5)

Down

1 Sculptures representing humans or animals (7)
2 Painkiller developed in Germany in the 1890s (7)
3 Civil or military authority in Turkey (5)
5 Sharp piercing cry (6)
6 Draft (6)
10 Evergreen tree with small berries and glossy aromatic leaves (3)
11 Device on an aircraft that controls lateral motion (7)
12 Adolescent (7)
14 Generator (6)
15 Walk unsteadily, as a small child (6)
18 Fen (5)

96

Across

2 Interpret (9)
6 Former Portuguese province on the south coast of China (5)
7 Wanders about (5)
9 Repent (3)
10 Unit of length (5)
12 Long-legged waterbird (5)
14 Come in (5)
17 Series of linked objects (5)
19 Garden tool (3)
20 Linger (5)
21 Girl who features in Lewis Carroll's famous stories (5)
22 Proximity (9)

Down

1 Soft, creamy French cheese (9)
2 Implied (5)
3 Shade of blue (5)
4 Fastener with a threaded shank (5)
5 Accolade (5)
8 Vast plain and National Park in Tanzania (9)
11 Cereal crop (3)
13 Anti-tobacco organisation (inits) (3)
15 Main part of the human body (5)
16 Piece of poetry (5)
17 Discontinue (5)
18 Haywire (5)

97

1			2		■	3	4			5
	■	■		■	6	■		■	■	
7		8		■	9					
	■	10				■		■	■	
11				■	12			13		■
	■		■	■		■	■		■	14
■	15		16			■	17			
18	■	■		■	19				■	
20						■	21			
	■	■		■		■		■	■	
22					■	23				

Across

1 Assembly of witches (5)
3 Markedly masculine in appearance or manner (5)
7 Source of illumination (4)
9 Characteristic of wolves (6)
10 Smallest particle in an element (4)
11 Being in a tense state (4)
12 Dais (5)
15 Raised medallion (5)
17 Capital of the Maldives (4)
19 Once ___ a time (4)
20 Abominable (6)
21 Waterbird that is black with a white beak (4)
22 Covering that protects an inside surface (5)
23 Forename of the wife of former US president Ronald Reagan (5)

Down

1 Visitor (6)
2 Hollow (5)
4 First letter of the Greek alphabet (5)
5 Due (4)
6 Place endowed for the support and lodging of the poor (9)
8 Molten rock (5)
13 Product of seabirds, used as a fertiliser (5)
14 In a mild, soft manner (6)
16 North American elk (5)
17 Coffee-chocolate drink (5)
18 Child's toy (4)

98

Across

1 Crude dwelling (5)
4 Sag (5)
7 Lyricist, ___ Gershwin (3)
8 Harvest (5)
10 Cook in an oven (5)
11 Grandmother (3)
12 Shatters violently (7)
13 Surreptitious (3)
15 Penultimate Greek letter (3)
17 Insistent (7)
20 Sense of self (3)
21 Gentleman's gentleman (5)
22 Illegal setting of fires (5)
23 Mrs Perón, second wife of former Argentinian president Juan Perón (3)
24 Weary (5)
25 Leaf that adorns the Canadian flag (5)

Down

1 Puts a name to (5)
2 Scene of action (5)
3 Having a merciful disposition (4-7)
4 Chief port of Tanzania (3,2,6)
5 Ellipses (5)
6 Substance used to secure panes of glass (5)
9 Artificial sources of visible illumination (5)
14 Characteristic language of a particular group (5)
15 Swivel (5)
16 Layabout (5)
18 Fabulist of ancient Greece (5)
19 Unit of weight (5)

1		2		3		4	■	5	■	6
	■		■		■	7	8			
9					■	10			■	
	■		■	11						
12			■		■	■		■	■	
■	■	13	14			15		16	■	■
17	■	■		■	■		■	18		19
20		21		22			■		■	
	■	23			■	24				
25					■		■		■	
	■		■	26						

99

Across

1 Imagined during sleep (7)
7 Come about (5)
9 Stand-in doctor (5)
10 Institute legal proceedings against (3)
11 Not at the scheduled time (7)
12 Beer (3)
13 Edge of a road or path (7)
18 Not processed or refined (3)
20 Attire (7)
23 World's second-largest living bird (3)
24 Existing (5)
25 Pertaining to hearing (5)
26 Everlasting (7)

Down

1 Fourth letter of the Greek alphabet (5)
2 Stay away from deliberately (6)
3 Recollection (6)
4 Give medicine to (4)
5 Very cold (4)
6 Wicker basket used to hold fish (5)
8 Healed (5)
14 Small terrestrial lizard (5)
15 Away from the coast (6)
16 Expensive white fur (6)
17 Heathen (5)
19 Unwanted plants (5)
21 Artificial waves in the hair (4)
22 Dominate (4)

100

Across

1 Item used to sweep the floor (5)

4 Nimble, spry (5)

7 Capital of Ontario (7)

8 Thing of value (5)

9 Persuade a person to buy worthless property (6)

12 Sweeping stroke or blow (5)

15 Airport in Chicago (5)

17 Reply (6)

18 Group of singers (5)

19 Overture (7)

20 Grind (teeth) (5)

21 Popular palm-like houseplant (5)

Down

1 Get around, circumvent (6)

2 Waterproof raincoat (7)

3 New Testament book (7)

5 Expansion (6)

6 Froth produced by soap (6)

10 Witchcraft (7)

11 Brief and to the point (7)

13 Network of rabbit burrows (6)

14 Sacred songs (6)

16 Printed mistakes (6)

101

Across

3 Be composed of (7)

6 Cause to be embarrassed (5)

7 Small guitar with four strings (7)

8 Relating to the Moon (5)

9 Following (4)

11 Mountain lion (4)

14 Always (4)

17 Marine crustacean (4)

19 Stratum (5)

20 Fissure in the Earth's crust (7)

21 Earnings (5)

22 Accuse of a wrong (7)

Down

1 Severe blow (6)

2 Large bottle of champagne (6)

3 Stir vigorously (5)

4 Military greeting (6)

5 Containing salt (6)

10 Geological period of time (3)

12 State of commotion and noise (6)

13 Tree with sharp thorns (6)

15 Ocean trip (6)

16 Most uncommon (6)

18 Moved by the wind (5)

102

Across

1 Island in Indonesia to the south of Borneo (4)
3 Aromatic herb (5)
6 Flightless bird (4)
8 Water flow resulting from sudden rain or melting snow (5)
9 Anticipated (8)
13 Rise upwards into the air (4)
15 Tolerant or lenient (3)
16 Native of Basra, eg (5)
17 Slang term for diamonds (3)
19 False belief (4)
21 Casserole of aubergine and ground lamb in a sauce (8)
24 Be superior to (5)
25 Partition (4)
26 Fashion (5)
27 Give a narcotic to (4)

Down

1 Christ (5)
2 Vessels that carry blood from the heart to the body (8)
3 Asked (4)
4 Father Christmas (5)
5 At high volume (4)
7 An evil spell (3)
10 Pedestrianised public square (5)
11 Culminated (8)
12 Get out (4)
14 Stew (4)
18 Asian dish (5)
20 Split fifty-fifty (5)
21 Bulk (4)
22 Dimensions (4)
23 Range of knowledge (3)

Across

1 Of a kind specified or understood (4)
3 Place of worship (6)
5 Expression of surprise (3)
6 Not in favour of (4)
7 Female organs of a flower (6)
9 Judicial remedy prohibiting a party from doing something (10)
14 US government unit (inits) (3)
15 And not (3)
17 Disk used to sharpen edge tools (10)
20 Cook (vegetables) briefly (6)
22 Part in a play (4)
23 Electrical resistance unit (3)
24 Long-tailed black and white crow (6)
25 Look good on (4)

Down

1 Motionless (6)
2 Japanese verse form (5)
3 Cloth hat (3)
4 Roll of hair worn at the nape of the neck (7)
8 Travel across snow (3)
10 TV chef, ___ Lawson (7)
11 Shock physically (3)
12 Rechewed food (3)
13 Yoko ___, widow of John Lennon (3)
16 Go back to a previous state (6)
18 Charged particle (3)
19 Limited periods of time (5)
21 Gardening tool (3)

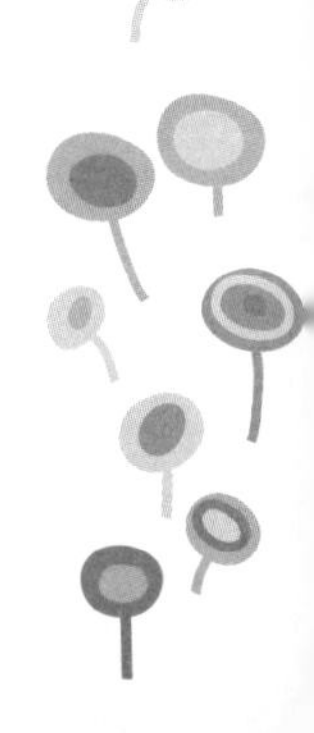

104

Across

4 Traveller who uses runners to cross snow (5)

7 Fleshy pendulous part of the hearing organ (7)

8 Hinged lifting tool (5)

9 Root vegetable (5)

10 Affianced (9)

13 Intermingle (5)

14 Aquatic creature (5)

15 Ireland's longest river (7)

16 Slender, graceful young woman (5)

Down

1 Biting tools (5)

2 Trophy usually awarded for winning third place in a competition (6,5)

3 Root used in the preparation of a sharp-tasting condiment (11)

4 Causing intense interest, stunning (11)

5 Arousing or holding the attention (11)

6 One who drives cars at high speeds (5)

11 Lies adjacent to or shares a boundary (5)

12 Former French unit of currency (5)

105

1			2		■	3	4	5		6
	■	■		■	7				■	
8					■	9				
	■	■		■	10	■		■	■	
11	12								13	
■		■		■		■		■		■
14										15
	■	■		■		■		■	■	
16		17		18	■	19				
	■	20				■		■	■	
21					■	22				

Across

1 Violent impact (5)
3 Bid (5)
7 Threesome (4)
8 Twin brother of Romulus (5)
9 Put up (5)
11 Town between Farnborough and Andover (11)
14 Coastal town in Dorset (11)
16 Dig into (5)
19 Excessive rate of interest (5)
20 Lean, tough and sinewy (4)
21 Basic unit of currency in many Arabian countries (5)
22 Coupling (5)

Down

1 Tree with edible pods used as a chocolate substitute (5)
2 Country, capital Riyadh (5,6)
3 Metal-bearing mineral (3)
4 Child of an aunt or uncle (5,6)
5 Adversary (3)
6 Bind again or anew (5)
10 Heron (5)
12 Bustle (3)
13 Case containing a set of articles (3)
14 Animal with two feet (5)
15 Composer, Joseph ___ (1732–1809) (5)
17 Be in possession of (3)
18 Make a mistake (3)

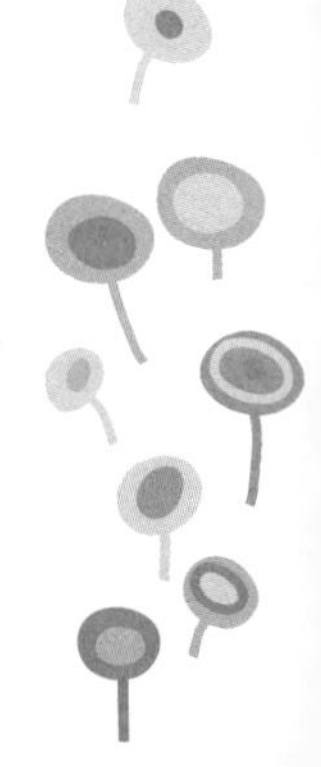

106

Across

1 Stout-bodied insect that produces a loud, chirping sound (6)

6 Influence by gentle urging (6)

8 Currency used in Kabul, for example (7)

9 Worn away (6)

10 Looks searchingly (5)

13 Quantity (7)

16 Belonging to the organ of smell (5)

18 Far from the intended target (6)

20 Largest anthropoid ape (7)

21 Person employed to buy and sell for others (6)

22 Without effort (6)

Down

1 Car wheel immobilising device (5)

2 On land (6)

3 Disease of the skin (4)

4 Draws aimlessly (7)

5 City on the River Aire (5)

7 Type of firearm (3,3)

11 Feeling (7)

12 Barbaric (6)

14 Hydrophobia (6)

15 Young sheep (5)

17 Having much foliage (5)

19 Past times (4)

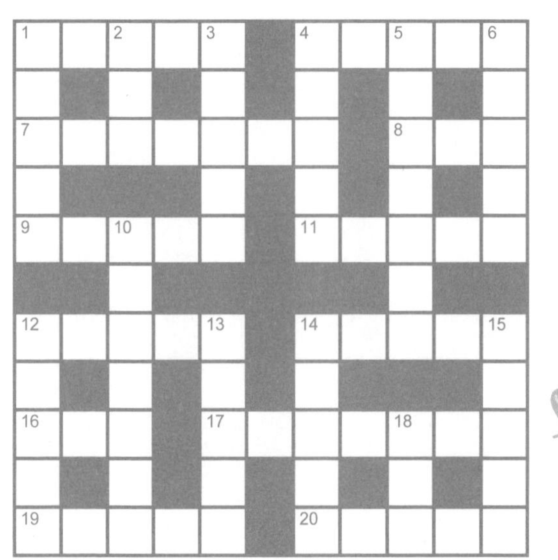

107

Across

1 Coagulated milk used to make cheese (5)

4 Prices (5)

7 Located in the open air (7)

8 Fish eggs (3)

9 Arctic marten (5)

11 Skin covering the top of the head (5)

12 Oil-bearing laminated rock (5)

14 Consecrate (5)

16 Moldovan monetary unit (3)

17 Oblivious (7)

19 Bread-raising agent (5)

20 Glossy fabric (5)

Down

1 Cuts into pieces, as with an axe (5)

2 Decompose (3)

3 Gradient (5)

4 Army unit of two or more divisions (5)

5 Family appellation (7)

6 Slumber (5)

10 Brilliant and showy technical skill (7)

12 Stupid, daft (5)

13 Express great joy (5)

14 Pulse vegetables (5)

15 Rear of a boat or ship (5)

18 Social insect (3)

108

Across

1 Skilled trades (6)

6 In a slumber (6)

7 Give a cat-like sound of pleasure (4)

8 Harsh criticism or disapproval (7)

10 Circuit (3)

12 Large entrance, reception room, or waiting area (11)

15 Geological period of time (3)

16 Shakespeare play (7)

19 Sea vessel (4)

20 Domed tent-like Native American dwelling (6)

21 Reflect deeply on a subject (6)

Down

1 Domed roof (6)

2 Exceedingly sudden and unexpected (6)

3 Mentally healthy (4)

4 European mountain range (4)

5 Request another supply (7)

8 Secret store of valuables or money (5)

9 Welsh town to the east of Swansea (5)

11 Substance taken to counter indigestion (7)

13 Further than (6)

14 Carnivorous bird, such as the eagle (6)

17 Basin (4)

18 Press down tightly (4)

109

Across

1 Noticeable deterioration in performance or quality (5)
3 Pierce with a needle (5)
7 Volcanic rock (4)
9 Musician, member of an orchestra (6)
10 Grudging feeling (4)
11 Yours and mine (4)
12 Flying insects with a formidable sting (5)
15 Grieve over a death (5)
17 Waste product useful as a fertiliser (4)
19 Hemispherical roof (4)
20 Look up to (6)
21 Twisted (4)
22 Cloth woven from flax (5)
23 Fertile tract in the desert (5)

Down

1 Unhealthy looking (6)
2 Has in mind (5)
4 Colloquial term for one's ancestry (5)
5 Long-tailed bird of prey of the hawk family (4)
6 Extremely talented young male (coll) (3,6)
8 Left-hand page (5)
13 Fruit pulp (5)
14 Insect that rests with forelimbs raised as if in prayer (6)
16 Combine (5)
17 Region of complete shadow (5)
18 Feeling of deep, bitter anger and ill-will (4)

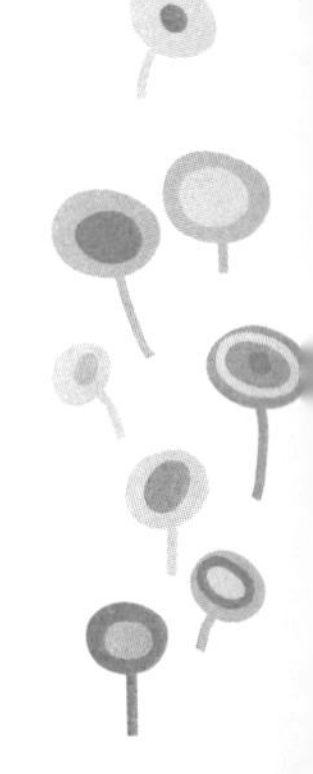

110

Across

1 Popular game played with pieces of stiffened paper (5)
4 Block used as a building or paving material (5)
7 Dressing for a wound (7)
8 Chronic drinker (3)
9 Mark (~) placed over the letter 'n' in Spanish (5)
11 Portable light (5)
12 Name given to a product (5)
14 Drinking tube (5)
16 Ground containing a mat of grass and grass roots (3)
17 Oblivious (7)
19 Flair (5)
20 Now (5)

Down

1 Ancient unit of length (5)
2 Went faster (3)
3 Quench (5)
4 Noise made by a sheep (5)
5 Underwriter (7)
6 Sailing vessel with two masts (5)
10 Date: 29 February (4,3)
12 Motor coaches (5)
13 Extinguish (5)
14 Tip at an angle (5)
15 Skinny, underweight (5)
18 Be of service (3)

111

Across

1 Social system that developed in Europe in the eighth century (9)
8 Having the leading position (5)
9 Particular items (5)
10 One of the two symbols used in Morse code (3)
11 Divine (5)
13 Chose (5)
15 Search, as with a dragnet (5)
18 Become liable to (5)
20 Mr Rush, football commentator (3)
21 Coils (5)
22 Country on the Iberian Peninsula (5)
23 Sweetheart (9)

Down

2 Change with a view to improving (5)
3 Informal term for a father (5)
4 Bingo (5)
5 Mixture of rain and snow (5)
6 In a proud or arrogant manner (9)
7 Toiletry article (9)
12 Depressed (3)
14 Greek deity, a cross between a man and a goat (3)
16 Forum in ancient Greece (5)
17 Cotton fabric used especially for hosiery and underwear (5)
18 Gusset (5)
19 Range of mountains (5)

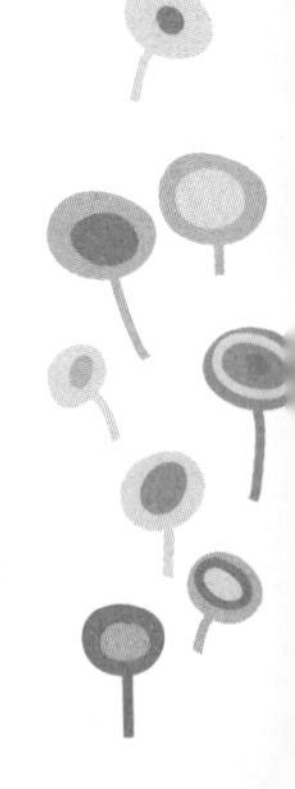

112

Across

1 Reclaimed from a wild state (5)
4 Musical half-note (5)
7 Boy (3)
8 Ask earnestly (7)
9 Enlist (5)
10 Strong, tightly twisted cotton thread (5)
12 Pale purple colour (5)
14 Addressed, covered (5)
16 Tramp, wanderer (7)
18 Measure of proficiency in judo (3)
19 Make a thrusting forward movement (5)
20 Large gathering of people (5)

Down

1 Flavour (5)
2 Dog of mixed breed (7)
3 Brood (on) (5)
4 Chemical element that can be formed into sheets (5)
5 Named prior to marriage (3)
6 Unit of length (5)
11 Malicious gossip (7)
12 Flat (5)
13 Lifting machine (5)
14 Discourage (5)
15 Tasting sour (5)
17 Alcoholic spirit (3)

Across

1 Sharpens (a razor) (6)
4 Clip at (4)
6 Banked oval track for bicycle or motorcycle racing (9)
8 One of four playing cards in a deck (3)
10 Madman (6)
13 Pale grey (4)
14 Emblem of Christianity (5)
16 Shoot (a gun) (4)
17 Stratagem, ploy (6)
20 Source of metal (3)
21 Cessation of normal operation (9)
22 Hooligans (4)
23 French sweet blackcurrant liqueur (6)

Down

1 Water vapour (5)
2 Bird associated with the Tower of London (5)
3 Column (6)
4 Ironical language (7)
5 Food in a pastry shell (3)
7 Angora yarn (6)
9 Salted roe of a sturgeon (6)
11 Masses of snow permanently covering the land (7)
12 Sprocket (3)
15 Small meat and vegetable turnover of Indian origin (6)
18 Fillip, incentive (5)
19 Portable shelters (usually of canvas) (5)
21 Purchase (3)

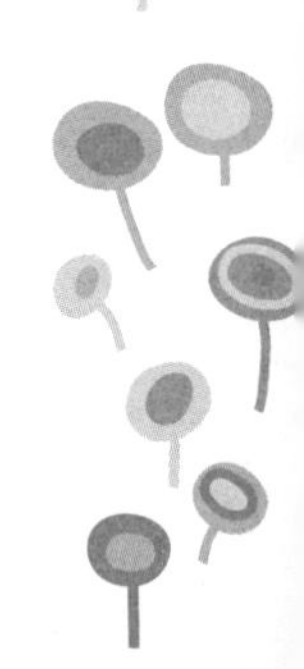

114

Across

1 Spanish word for 'tomorrow' (6)
6 Nerve cell (6)
7 Relaxation (4)
9 Fleshy edible fruit with a tuft of stiff leaves (9)
13 Copy on thin paper (5)
15 Charge a contribution to state revenue (3)
16 Slang term for diamonds (3)
17 Employ (3)
19 Equip in advance for a particular purpose (5)
23 Long strings of pasta (9)
25 Encourage (4)
26 Appraisal of the value of something (6)
27 Protective fold of skin (6)

Down

1 Be worthy or deserving (5)
2 Trick (5)
3 Gambling stake (4)
4 Church cellar (5)
5 Attach to (5)
8 Bathing resort (3)
10 Characteristic sound made by a horse (5)
11 Vigilant (5)
12 Alight (4)
14 Coarse file (4)
17 Commandeer (5)
18 Foxhole (5)
20 Short composition for a solo instrument (5)
21 Melody (3)
22 Bear fruit (5)
24 Boundary, rim (4)

Across

1 Subject matter of a conversation (5)
4 Country, capital Kathmandu (5)
7 Back part of the neck (4)
9 Become worse or disintegrate (11)
10 Young people (6)
12 Professional charges (4)
13 Quarrel about petty points (4)
14 Safe place (6)
17 Morbid fear of open spaces (11)
20 James ___, US film actor (1931–55) (4)
21 Nude (5)
22 Ermine in its brown summer coat (5)

Down

1 Child's toy bear (5)
2 Generally incompetent (5)
3 Motor vehicle (3)
4 Prefix meaning recent or modern (3)
5 Flat upland (7)
6 City in Yorkshire (5)
8 Very narrow band pattern in cloth, especially of the type used for formal suits (9)
11 Discharge from the priesthood (7)
13 Locomotive (5)
15 Forepart (5)
16 Raise to a higher rank or position (5)
18 Append (3)
19 Features (3)

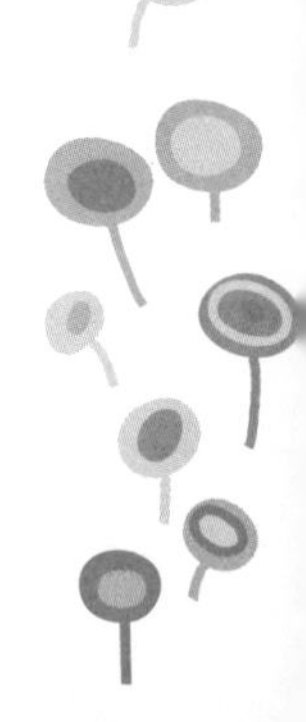

116

Across

2 English conspirator celebrated on 5 November (3,6)
7 Substance for staining or colouring (3)
8 Gathered, as of natural products (7)
10 Taster (7)
12 Drama (4)
13 Lush greenness of flourishing vegetation (7)
14 Level (4)
16 Itinerant Australian labourer (7)
19 Spurting intermittently (7)
20 Title (3)
21 Full agreement between a number of people (9)

Down

1 Make suitable for a new purpose (5)
2 Unit of heredity (4)
3 One who has achieved a high level of spiritual insight (4)
4 Not many (1,3)
5 Catch fire (6)
6 Unhappily (5)
9 Disappointment (3-4)
11 Change direction (4)
12 Self-consciously precise person (4)
13 Small animals or insects that are pests (6)
14 Subject (5)
15 Very cross (5)
16 Face (4)
17 Becomes older (4)
18 Bulk (4)

1			2	3	■	4			5	
	■	■	6				■	■		■
7					■	8	9			
	■	■		■	10	■		■		■
11	12									
■		■		■		■		■		■
13										14
■		■		■		■		■	■	
15				16	■	17				
■		■	■	18				■	■	
19					■	20				

117

Across

1 Crouch, bow (5)
4 Close-fitting (5)
6 Chess piece (4)
7 Pale (5)
8 Russian rulers (5)
11 Psychological state characterised by delusions of grandeur (11)
13 Acquaint, make conversant with (11)
15 Recipient of money (5)
17 Computer instruction that results in a series of instructions (5)
18 In the way indicated (4)
19 Army doctor (5)
20 Make do (3,2)

Down

1 Group of many insects (5)
2 Being in force (9)
3 Metal cooking vessel (3)
4 Yellow-coloured explosive compound (inits) (3)
5 Vainglorious, extravagant or melodramatic conduct (7)
9 Set of steps (9)
10 Acute abdominal pain (5)
12 Issue forth (7)
14 Hard black wood (5)
16 And so forth (abbr) (3)
17 Drinking vessel (3)

118

Across

1 Implied (5)
4 Humble (5)
7 Constricted (6)
9 Graven image (4)
11 Religious cult practised chiefly in Caribbean countries (6)
12 Cavalryman (6)
14 Minute life-form (4)
16 Daybreak (4)
19 Bunch of cords tied at one end (6)
22 Official responsible for managing and protecting an area of forest (6)
23 Deposit of valuable ore (4)
24 Scattered wreckage (6)
25 Coat with fat during cooking (5)
26 Make angry (5)

Down

1 Severely damaged by tearing or crushing (7)
2 Protective garment (5)
3 Treasure of unknown ownership (5)
5 Hollywood's Beau, Jeff and Lloyd (7)
6 Trail left by an animal (5)
8 Tightly twisted woollen yarn (7)
10 Female deer (3)
13 Unite (7)
15 Sweet Madeira wine (7)
17 Bouquet (5)
18 Small mass of soft material (3)
20 Battleground (5)
21 Enchantress (5)

119

Across

1 Spectacle (5)
3 Journal (5)
6 Leaves out (5)
7 Prime minister of India from 1947 to 1964 (5)
10 Refreshing soft drink (5,6)
13 Good fellowship (11)
15 Edge tool used in shaving (5)
18 Legend (5)
19 Spy (5)
20 Type of boat used to transport people and cars (5)

Down

1 Large group of fish (5)
2 Difficult situation (coll) (3,6)
3 Teacher at a university or college (3)
4 Fire residue (3)
5 Juvenility (5)
8 Determine the amount of (9)
9 US Academy Award (5)
11 Ms Braun, Hitler's mistress (3)
12 Narrow runner used for gliding over snow (3)
13 Stoppers for bottles, etc (5)
14 Adversary, foe (5)
16 Menagerie (3)
17 Tear apart (3)

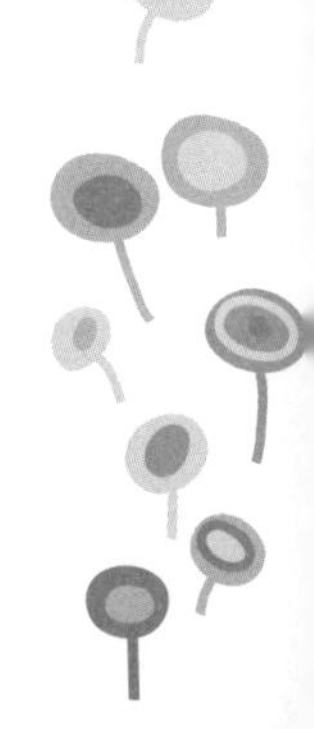

120

Across

1 Salve, ointment (4)
3 Provide a brief summary (5)
6 Gifted, competent (4)
7 Box lightly (4)
9 Decompose (3)
10 Pupil (7)
12 Sporting trophy (3)
13 Fruit of a rose plant (3)
14 Trade stoppage (7)
15 Primitive fish (3)
16 Chafe (3)
18 Ability to walk steadily on the deck of a pitching ship (3,4)
20 Greek letter (3)
21 Edward ___, British artist and poet (4)
22 Fencing sword (4)
23 Admitted to something (5)
24 Appellation (4)

Down

1 Fundamental (5)
2 Trading place (4)
3 Practise (8)
4 Draught animal (9)
5 Raise, erect (3,2)
8 Disparaging remark (9)
11 Characterised by a lack of partiality (8)
15 Harmless tropical house-lizard (5)
17 Carried (5)
19 Scottish valley (4)

121

1			2	■	3				4	
	■	■	5			■	■	■		■
6				■	7		8			
	■	■		■		■		■		■
9	10	11						12		■
13				■	■	■	14			15
■	16				17					
■		■		■		■		■	■	
18						■	19			
■		■	■	■	20			■	■	
21						■	22			

Across

1 ___ Guinness, actor who played Ben 'Obi-wan' Kenobi in the *Star Wars* movies (4)
3 Small pouch for shampoo, etc (6)
5 Cereal grass (3)
6 Standard (4)
7 Antipathetic (6)
9 Across the country (10)
13 Surfeit (4)
14 Banking system (4)
16 Item appended to an email (10)
18 Resist separation (6)
19 Roman cloak (4)
20 ___ Lanka, country (3)
21 Feeling of ill-will arousing active hostility (6)
22 Spanish sparkling white wine (4)

Down

1 Canopy (6)
2 Group delegated to consider some matter (9)
3 Dye or other colouring material (5)
4 From the Orient (7)
8 Mysterious (9)
10 Character in the *Arabian Nights* (7)
11 Expression of disapproval (3)
12 Gaming cube (3)
15 Capital of Canada (6)
17 Green salad vegetable (5)

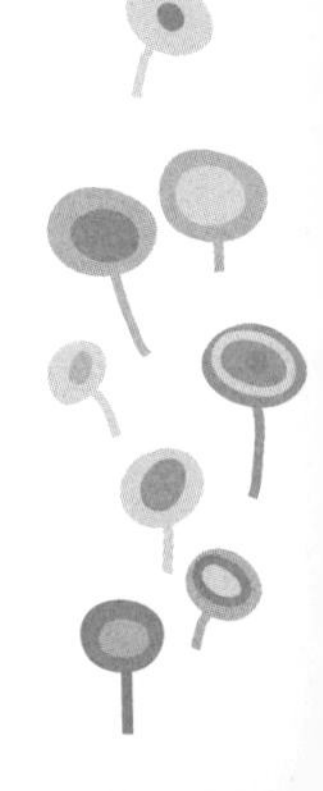

122

Across

1 Quick and energetic (5)
4 Brittle fragment (5)
7 Fuse (4)
9 Saying: "___ is next to godliness" (11)
10 Metallic element, symbol Na (6)
12 Small gentle horse (4)
13 Number indicated by the Roman V (4)
14 Job (6)
17 Action of keeping something harmful under control or within limits (11)
20 Blackleg (4)
21 Believe (5)
22 Gapes (5)

Down

1 Gives one's support or approval to (5)
2 Hindu religious teacher (5)
3 Family (3)
4 Travel on the piste (3)
5 Plant also known as the windflower (7)
6 Lit by twilight (5)
8 Causing a concluding action (9)
11 Leonardo ___, Italian artist, engineer, scientist and architect (1452–1519) (2,5)
13 Aspect (5)
15 Ballroom dance of Cuban origin (5)
16 Local tax on property (5)
18 Enquire (3)
19 Word indicating a negative answer (3)

123

Across

1 Bottomless gulf or pit (poetic) (5)
5 Stocky short-legged harness horse (3)
7 Coiffure (6)
8 Baffling question or problem (5)
10 Rise rapidly, rush (5)
11 Admit one's guilt (7)
14 Wanderer with no fixed abode or employment (7)
16 Statement of beliefs (5)
17 Cow's milk-gland (5)
19 Citrus fruit (6)
20 2240 pounds (3)
21 Delight (5)

Down

1 Domesticated llama with long silky fleece (6)
2 H Rider Haggard novel (3)
3 Mrs Simpson, Bart Simpson's mother (5)
4 Tie the limbs of a bird before cooking (5)
5 Small garden surrounded by walls or buildings (9)
6 Foundation (4)
9 Person who is not married or in a relationship (9)
12 Bathing resort (3)
13 Floor of a house (6)
14 Vociferous (5)
15 Distance between the wheels of a railway train (5)
16 Insincere talk about religion or morals (4)
18 Hideout (3)

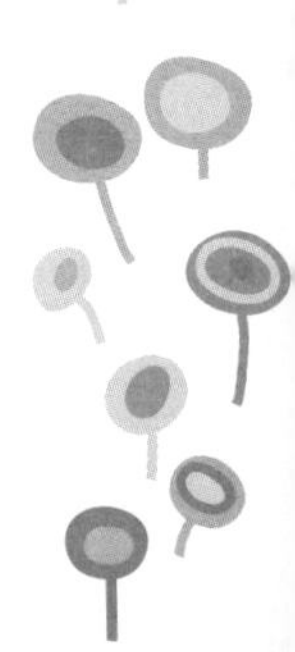

124

Across

1 Ride the waves of the sea on a board (4)
3 British snake (5)
6 Probabilities (4)
7 Close by (4)
9 Variety of peach (9)
11 Mexican comrade (5)
12 Colossus (7)
15 Ordain (5)
17 Translate (9)
18 Keep in check (4)
19 Encircle (4)
20 Cher's former singing partner (5)
21 Involuntary intake of breath through a wide open mouth (4)

Down

1 Father Christmas (5)
2 Be earlier in time, precede (6)
3 Enquire as to the wellbeing of (3,5)
4 Belittle (9)
5 Watercourse (5)
8 General activity and motion (9)
10 In an opposing direction (8)
13 Enterprising or ambitious drive (6)
14 Married women (5)
16 Projection shaped to fit into a mortise (5)

125

Across

1 Nap (5)
3 Freshwater fish (5)
6 Poker stake (4)
8 After (6)
10 Present (5)
12 Small bottle that contains a drug (5)
14 Public sale (7)
15 Plague, annoy continually (5)
16 Wide open (5)
18 Faults (6)
19 Place in the post (4)
20 Painting applied to a wall surface (5)
21 Biased way of presenting something (5)

Down

1 Astute (5)
2 The night before (3)
3 Theatrical performer (8)
4 Bring into being (9)
5 Relating to sea movements (5)
7 Financial officer (9)
9 Muscle of the chest (8)
11 Repent (3)
13 Domestic swine (3)
15 Freshwater fish (5)
17 Empower (5)
19 Serious offence (3)

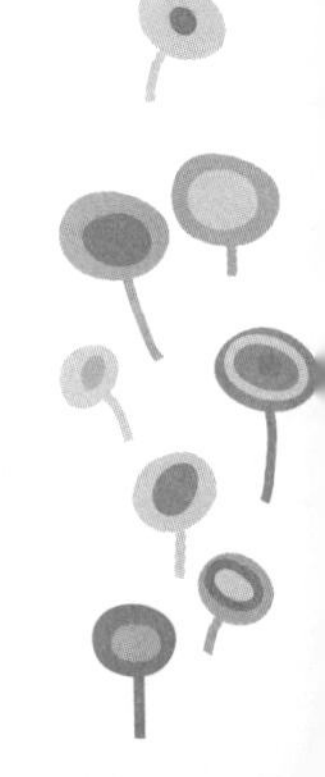

126

Across

1 Perspiration (5)
4 Wed (5)
7 Ludicrous acts done for fun (6)
9 Cinema attendant (5)
10 Female servant (4)
11 On a plane (6)
13 Hardy cabbage with coarse curly leaves (4)
16 Sediment in wine (4)
18 Give in to, indulge (6)
20 Mixer drink (4)
21 Organ of a flower (5)
22 Greek 'L' (6)
23 Cast off hair, skin or feathers (5)
24 Divisions of the school year (5)

Down

1 Delivered a blow to (6)
2 Mexican tortilla (9)
3 Diadem (5)
5 Creature (6)
6 Inhabit (6)
8 Custodian (9)
12 Stinging insect (3)
14 Mythological god of light and day (6)
15 Substance covering the crown of a tooth (6)
17 Record player needle (6)
19 Cook with dry heat (5)

127

Across

4 Style of glazed pottery (5)
7 Pear-shaped fruit (7)
8 Shake (3)
10 Had better (5)
12 Sibling's daughter (5)
13 Animal's home (4)
15 Very cordial (9)
19 Cipher (4)
21 Yawns wide (5)
24 Religious doctrine (5)
25 Viper (3)
26 Made up of famous top performers (3-4)
27 Make a rhythmic sound with the fingers (5)

Down

1 Cured pig's meat (5)
2 Hinged switch that can assume either of two positions (6)
3 Acid found in milk (6)
4 Duck's feathers (4)
5 Racing toboggan (4)
6 River that flows through Rome (5)
9 Japanese martial art (6)
11 Cuts in two equal pieces (6)
14 Legendary bird (3)
16 Self-contained component (6)
17 Invalidate (6)
18 Representative (5)
20 Mr Humphries, aka Dame Edna Everage (5)
22 Set of two (4)
23 Unwanted email (4)

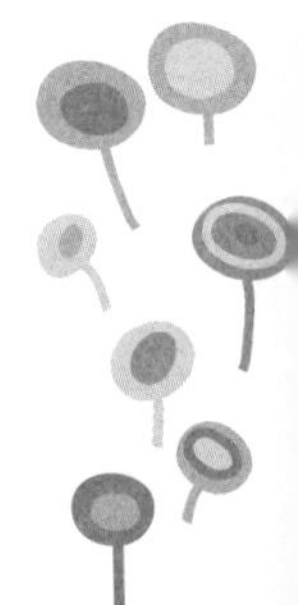

128

Across

1 French brandy (6)
6 Fill with optimism (6)
7 Harsh or corrosive in tone (6)
8 Indistinct or hazy in outline (6)
10 Lure (5)
13 Without weapons (7)
16 Attack (5)
18 Song of devotion or loyalty (6)
20 Frozen spike (6)
21 Short underpants (6)
22 Small stamp or seal on a ring (6)

Down

1 Diced (5)
2 Country (6)
3 Inhibit (4)
4 Sorcerers (7)
5 Remains in place (5)
9 Large luxurious car (abbr) (4)
11 Barrier to vision (7)
12 US university (4)
14 Ceasing (6)
15 Perhaps (5)
17 River that flows through Nottingham (5)
19 Fail to hit (4)

129

1		2		3	■	4		5		6
	■		■	7			■		■	
8			9		■	10				
	■	11			12		■		■	
13	14			■	15		16		17	
■		■		■		■		■		■
18		19		20		■	21	22		23
	■		■	24		25			■	
26					■	27				
	■		■	28			■		■	
29					■	30				

Across

1 Hazes over (5)
4 Makes tight against leakage (5)
7 Cardinal number (3)
8 Sketched (5)
10 Not a single person (2-3)
11 Endures (5)
13 Requests (4)
15 Reposed (6)
18 Surpassing in quality (6)
21 Sums up (4)
24 Belonging to them (5)
26 Chocolate powder (5)
27 Level (5)
28 Boisterous practical joke (3)
29 Dish out (5)
30 Relative magnitude (5)

Down

1 Means for communicating information (5)
2 Follow prey stealthily (5)
3 Male children (4)
4 General conscious awareness (5)
5 In the area or vicinity (5)
6 Swiftness (5)
9 Fritter away (5)
12 Accuracy (5)
14 Travel on the piste (3)
16 Step (5)
17 Conclude (3)
18 Confronts bravely (5)
19 More pleasant (5)
20 Look at intently (5)
22 Excitement (5)
23 Panorama (5)
25 Ova (4)

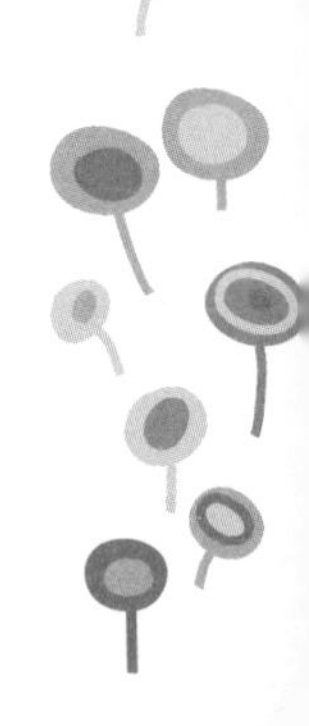

130

Across

3 Enchant (7)
6 Eighth letter of the Greek alphabet (5)
7 Humorous axiom stating that anything that can go wrong will go wrong (4,3)
8 Commercial exchange (5)
9 Cut or eliminate (6)
12 Expectorate (4)
15 Component (4)
17 Deserved by one's efforts (6)
19 Revolving arm of a distributor (5)
20 Existing, whether with lawful authority or not (2,5)
21 Relish served with food (5)
22 Plans for attaining a particular goal (7)

Down

1 Position of a person in society (6)
2 Emblems of high office (7)
3 Founded (5)
4 Arch of the foot (6)
5 Drink to follow immediately after another drink (6)
10 Organ of sight (3)
11 Display of bad temper (7)
13 Formerly the basic unit of money in Spain (6)
14 Absentee, especially one without permission (6)
16 Conservatives (6)
18 Worthless material (5)

Across

1 Scribble (6)
4 Becomes older (4)
6 Political system governed by a single individual (9)
8 Imaginary monster or ogre (3)
10 Regional dialect (6)
13 Act presumptuously (4)
14 Trap for birds or small mammals (5)
16 Prescribed selection of foods (4)
17 One of Santa's reindeer (6)
20 Consumption (3)
21 Final peremptory demand (9)
22 Close by, near (4)
23 Plant with spiny bracts (6)

Down

1 Sailing vessel with a single mast (5)
2 Show a response (5)
3 On the inside (6)
4 Rubs hard, roughens (7)
5 Outer space as viewed from Earth (3)
7 Dental decay (6)
9 Having spokes (6)
11 Fast-running African flightless bird (7)
12 Melancholy (3)
15 Baby's plaything (6)
18 Organic component of soil (5)
19 Kingly, majestic (5)
21 Container for ashes (3)

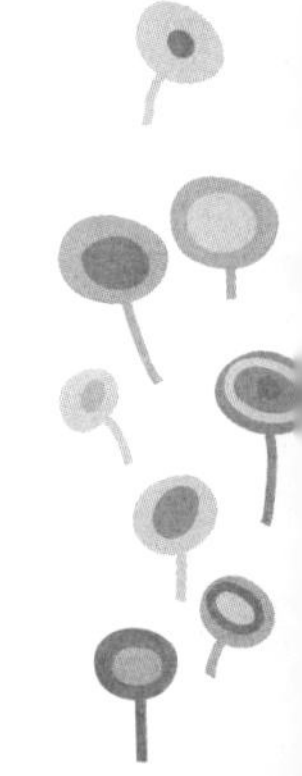

132

Across

- **3** Christen (7)
- **6** On your own (5)
- **7** Derived by logic, without observed facts (1,6)
- **8** Form of civil disobedience (3-2)
- **9** Location (4)
- **11** Moves the head in agreement (4)
- **14** Long journey (4)
- **17** Create (4)
- **19** Clemency (5)
- **20** Point at which to retire for the night (7)
- **21** Angry dispute (3-2)
- **22** Man devoted to the pursuit of pleasure (7)

Down

- **1** Person authorised to conduct religious worship (6)
- **2** Ransacked (6)
- **3** Vegetables (5)
- **4** Bathroom fixture (6)
- **5** Scratch (6)
- **10** Liquid used for printing (3)
- **12** Difficult experience (6)
- **13** Forge (6)
- **15** Impatient (6)
- **16** Regulating the musical pitch of (6)
- **18** ___ board, used to shape fingernails (5)

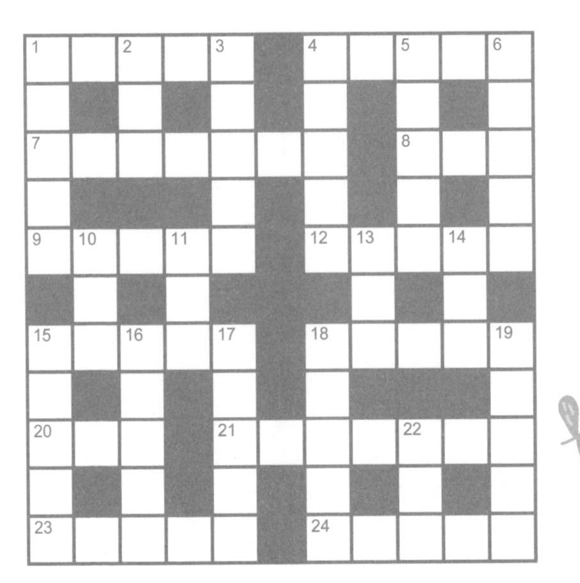

133

Across

1 Picture puzzle (5)
4 Fowl's perch (5)
7 Garden flower (7)
8 Plaything (3)
9 Pantomime women (5)
12 Cut into small pieces (5)
15 Piece of pipe that bends backwards on itself (1-4)
18 Aids (5)
20 Young carnivore (3)
21 Tube that conveys air in and out of the lungs (7)
23 Hooded jacket (5)
24 Storehouse (5)

Down

1 Quick, fast (5)
2 Automated computer program for doing a particular task (3)
3 Musical compositions with words (5)
4 Kingdom (5)
5 Many times (5)
6 Aromatic herb (5)
10 Pertinent (3)
11 Recede (3)
13 Extreme anger (3)
14 Football trophy (3)
15 Remove a lid (5)
16 Natural brown earth pigment (5)
17 Crowd actor (5)
18 Secret store (5)
19 Vertical passage into a mine (5)
22 Pelvic joint (3)

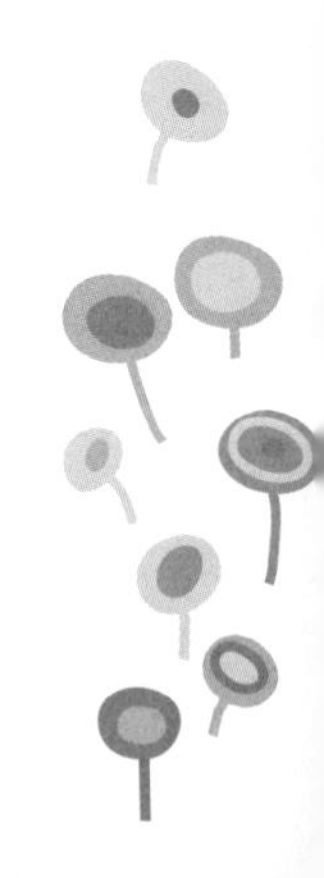

134

Across

1 Give birth to (4)
3 Bowed, curved (6)
5 Gall (3)
6 Compact mass (of earth) (4)
7 Sour-tasting (6)
9 Container for clothing, sheets, etc that need washing (5,6)
14 Device that is very useful for a particular job (11)
18 Thoroughfare (6)
20 Part of a skeleton (4)
21 Be unwell (3)
22 Beetle considered divine by Ancient Egyptians (6)
23 Way out (4)

Down

1 Idyllically rustic (7)
2 Long raised strip (5)
3 Alias (inits) (3)
4 Leave or strike out, as of vowels (5)
8 Uncertainties, doubtful factors, ___ and buts (3)
10 Female member of a religious order (3)
11 Long fluffy scarf (3)
12 Colourful ornamental fish (3)
13 Line touching a curve (7)
15 Of the eye (5)
16 Stand for a golf ball (3)
17 Item of furniture (5)
19 Metal ring that is pulled to open a can (3)

Across

1 Deceive (5)

5 Quarrel (3)

7 Run off to marry (5)

8 Code of beliefs accepted as authoritative (5)

9 Small fish (7)

11 Lamp (7)

13 Love affair (7)

15 Filled tortilla (7)

16 Attempted (5)

17 Daughter of one's brother (5)

18 Flexible container with a single opening (3)

19 Water ice on a small wooden stick (5)

Down

1 Embrace lovingly (6)

2 Applied science (11)

3 Banter (5)

4 Grieve (5)

5 Occupied by private houses (11)

6 Sagacious (4)

10 Jargon (5)

12 Extremely poisonous or injurious (6)

13 Passenger (5)

14 Drivers' stopover (5)

15 Incandescent lamp (4)

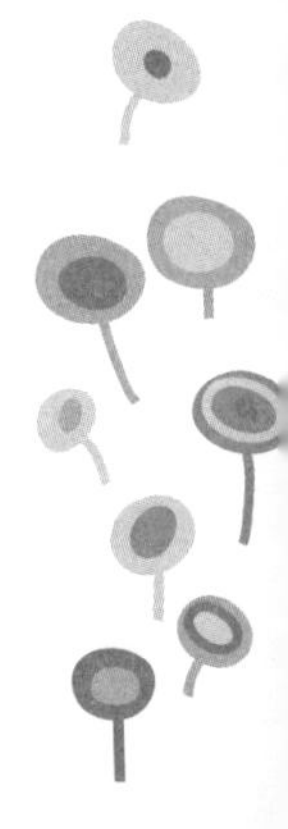

136

Across

1 Cloth (6)
6 Radio antenna (6)
7 Universe (6)
9 Experienced, competent (7)
10 Reef of coral (5)
12 Colonist (7)
17 Nearsighted person (5)
18 Japanese warrior (7)
20 Bring into existence (6)
21 Bumper car (6)
22 "I have found it" (6)

Down

1 Beauty treatment involving massage and cleansing (6)
2 Chess piece (6)
3 Barrel (4)
4 Basket on wheels (7)
5 Went out with, courted (5)
8 European capital city once called Christiania (4)
11 Christian sacrament commemorating the Last Supper (7)
13 Islamic ruler (4)
14 Go round and round (6)
15 Groups containing one or more species (6)
16 Commissioned military officer (5)
19 Highest level attainable (4)

1	■	2	■	3	■	4		5		6
7							■		■	
	■		■		■		■		■	
8			9		10		11			
	■	■		■		■		■	■	
■	12									■
13	■	■		■		■		■	■	14
15		16		17		18		19		
	■		■		■		■		■	
	■		■	20						
21					■		■		■	

137

Across

4 Smudge, daub (5)
7 Contemplative (7)
8 Small paving slab with curved top, once used to make roads (11)
12 Measuring land heights and distances for mapping purposes (9)
15 Seizing control of a vehicle by the use of force (11)
20 Spanish painter, born in Greece (1541–1614) (2,5)
21 Foolish or senseless behaviour (5)

Down

1 Producing a hot sensation on the taste buds (5)
2 Handle (4)
3 Cash register (4)
4 Stitches together (4)
5 EU monetary unit (4)
6 Honey-badger of Africa and southern Asia (5)
9 Delivery (5)
10 Clyster (5)
11 Dense (5)
13 Husks of wheat or other seed separated by threshing (5)
14 Inuit dwelling (5)
16 Ambition, aim (4)
17 Australian term for a young kangaroo (4)
18 Container for a bird (4)
19 Mountain goat (4)

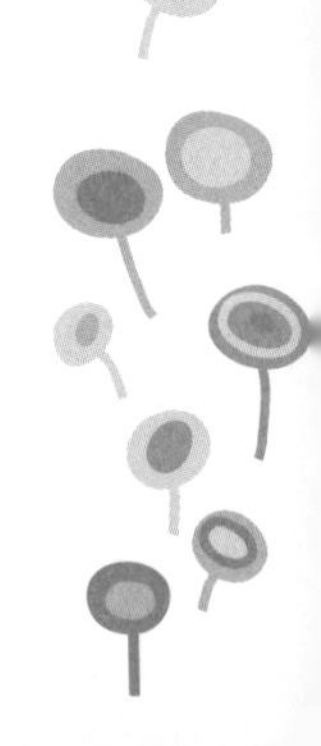

138

Across

1 Puts into order (5)
4 Great danger (5)
7 Highly excited (4)
8 Short formal piece of writing (5)
9 Make warm (4)
10 Time assigned on a schedule or agenda (4)
12 Japanese drink made from fermented rice (4)
15 Back part of a shoe (4)
17 Aggressive and pointed remark (4)
19 Challenge to do something dangerous (4)
20 Ruptures (5)
22 Ready money (4)
23 Brag (5)
24 Debonair (5)

Down

1 Emphasis (6)
2 British explorer of the Arctic and Antarctic (4)
3 Corset (5)
5 One half of a quarter (6)
6 Pierce with a sharp stake (6)
11 Science room (abbr) (3)
13 Slowly, in musical tempo (6)
14 Kicks out (6)
16 Canine film star (6)
18 Attitude, beliefs (5)
21 Verdi opera with an Egyptian theme (4)

139

Across

1 Moral principles (6)
6 Public speaker (6)
7 Rough with small waves (6)
9 Face veil worn by Muslim women (7)
11 Buddy (3)
13 Tutor's favourite student (8,3)
16 Burned remains (3)
17 Love affair (7)
20 Relating to or similar to bears (6)
21 Fin on the back of a fish (6)
22 Discover the site of (6)

Down

1 Apart from (6)
2 Fairground game of ring throwing (4-2)
3 Asian plant widely cultivated for its oily beans (4)
4 German composer (1685–1750) (4)
5 Gives to a charity or good cause (7)
8 Large snake (6)
10 Person who browses on the internet (6)
12 Spray can (7)
14 Verdigris (6)
15 Steal something (6)
18 As well (4)
19 Reduce the population of (animals) by selective slaughter (4)

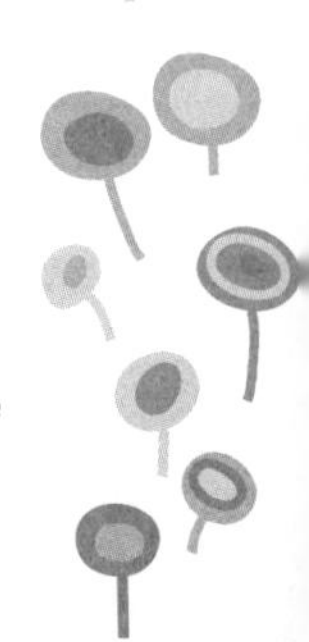

140

Across

1 Miscellaneous unspecified objects (5)
4 Troublesome children (5)
7 Larva of a butterfly or moth (11)
8 Alone (4)
11 Children's outdoor toy (6)
14 Clandestine (6)
17 Weapons (4)
21 Set of questions evaluating knowledge (11)
22 Military vehicles (5)
23 Fillip, incentive (5)

Down

1 Fires from a job (5)
2 Up to a time that (5)
3 Gardening tool used for digging (4)
4 Groom's partner (5)
5 Map book (5)
6 Drinking tube (5)
9 Single number (3)
10 Scull (3)
11 Took a chair (3)
12 Period of time (3)
13 Direct (3)
14 Aroma (5)
15 Range of mountains (5)
16 Departs (5)
18 Govern (5)
19 Musical compositions with words (5)
20 Charles ___, English essayist (1775–1834) (4)

1	■	2	■	3			4		5	
6					■	■		■		■
	■		■	7						
8					■	■		■		■
	■		■	9	10			■		■
11	12		13	■		■	14	15		16
■		■	17			18	■		■	
■		■		■	■	19				
20							■		■	
■		■		■	■	21				
22							■		■	

Across

3 Ask advice from (7)

6 Transmitting live (2-3)

7 Skilled craftsman (7)

8 Prophets (5)

9 A few (4)

11 Compass point (4)

14 English flower (4)

17 Skating area (4)

19 Decree (5)

20 Lose hope (7)

21 Plant used in the making of tequila (5)

22 Light spear thrown in a competitive sport (7)

Down

1 Foam used in hair styling (6)

2 Stroke tenderly (6)

3 Uncouth (5)

4 Tremble with cold (6)

5 Goes (6)

10 Possess (3)

12 Mrs Merkel, Chancellor of Germany (6)

13 Threefold (6)

15 Passé (slang) (3,3)

16 Deserved by one's efforts (6)

18 Holy book of Islam (5)

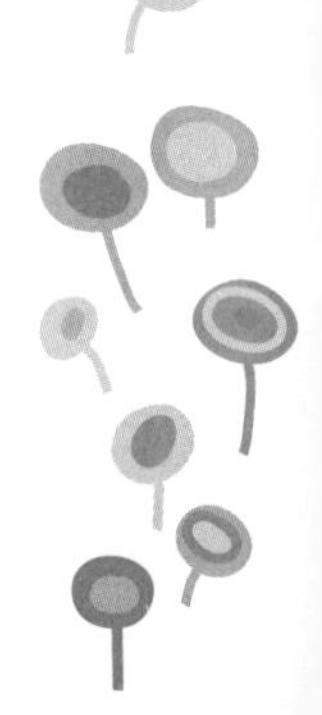

142

Across

1 Gives temporarily (5)
4 Lacking cash (5)
7 Basic unit of currency in Nicaragua (7)
8 Devon river (3)
9 Wood-turning tool (5)
11 Tartan (5)
12 Cringe (5)
14 Soothing unction (5)
16 Delivery vehicle (3)
17 Highly-prized edible subterranean fungus (7)
19 Imperial (5)
20 Giddy (5)

Down

1 In the area (5)
2 Scottish port (3)
3 Retail establishment (5)
4 Skin covering the top of the head (5)
5 On the whole (7)
6 Pace (5)
10 Period of occupancy (7)
12 Vacillate (5)
13 Sing the praises of (5)
14 Small army unit (5)
15 Mournful poem for the dead (5)
18 Felt cap of Morocco (3)

143

Across

1 Small amount of food eaten between meals (5)

4 Quarry (3)

6 Retch (5)

7 Minor actor in crowd scenes (5)

9 Former capital of Pakistan (7)

11 Biographical sketch (7)

13 Knead (7)

15 Mixture of decaying vegetation and manure (7)

16 Set straight or right (5)

17 Region of eastern South Africa, KwaZulu-___ (5)

18 Concert featuring bands (3)

19 Offspring of a male lion and female tiger (5)

Down

1 Treeless Russian plain (6)

2 Military fabric (5)

3 Former name of the Democratic Republic of Congo (5)

4 Penetrate gradually (9)

5 Hackney carriage (4)

8 Not being faithful to a spouse or lover (3-6)

10 Pseudonym (5)

12 Given to sympathy or gentleness (6)

13 Opening through which food is taken in (5)

14 Cause an engine to stop (5)

15 Wooden shoe (4)

144

Across

1 Give rise to (5)
3 Desert watering hole (5)
7 Shelled, aquatic reptile (6)
9 Knowledge gained through tradition (4)
10 Incapable of being avoided (10)
14 Small barrel (3)
16 Duty that is essential and urgent (10)
19 State of disorder (4)
20 Aim at (6)
22 Strong winds (5)
23 Take as one's own (5)

Down

1 Male pollen-bearing cluster on a hazel tree (6)
2 Division of a tennis match (3)
4 Perform without preparation (2-3)
5 Wooden vehicle on runners (4)
6 Adroitness in using the hands (9)
8 Watery discharge from the eyes or nose (5)
11 US musician and record producer, ___ Turner (3)
12 ___ Khan (3)
13 Deviating from the truth (5)
15 Instruction to go away (4,2)
17 Out of fashion (5)
18 Complacent (4)
21 Fishing tool (3)

145

Across

1 Pieces of food on a skewer (5)
4 Put to shame (5)
7 Egotistical (4)
8 Young of an eel (5)
9 Domesticates (5)
11 Coins kept about one's person for small expenditures (5,6)
15 Indian state, capital Panaji (3)
16 Revise the terms of (11)
19 Not affected by alcohol (5)
21 Lubricated (5)
22 Reverse an action (4)
23 Mike ___, former champion boxer (5)
24 Medium that was once supposed to fill all space (5)

Down

1 Rest on bended legs (5)
2 Affirms solemnly and formally (5)
3 Exclude (3)
4 Punk rocker Stuart Goddard, better known as Adam ___ (3)
5 Country, capital Yerevan (7)
6 Hermann ___, author of *Steppenwolf* (5)
10 Large ladle (5)
12 Motorcoach (7)
13 Ovum (3)
14 Item worn on the head (3)
16 Take (an examination) again (5)
17 Imbecile (5)
18 Duck valued for its soft down (5)
20 Sprint (3)
21 Lyric poem (3)

146

Across

1 Discordant (3,2,4)

7 Once more (5)

8 Appliance that removes moisture (5)

9 Prompt (3)

10 Burn superficially or lightly (5)

12 Proportion (5)

14 Subsist on a meagre allowance (5)

17 Welsh breed of dog (5)

19 Atmosphere (3)

20 Berkshire town, famous for its racecourse (5)

21 Literary composition (5)

22 Inhabitants (9)

Down

2 Educate in a skill (5)

3 Receiver of stolen goods (5)

4 Below (5)

5 Arab republic (5)

6 Inquisitiveness (9)

7 Helper (9)

11 Precious or semi-precious stone (3)

13 Bustle (3)

15 Bring upon oneself (5)

16 Routes (5)

17 Religious doctrine (5)

18 Plant substance (5)

147

Across

1 Occasions for buying at lower prices (5)
3 *The Mill on the ___*, George Eliot novel (5)
6 Dominate (4)
8 Unit of electric current (6)
10 Closely crowded together (5)
12 Very recently (5)
14 Decorate (7)
15 Blacksmith's workplace (5)
16 Exhausted (5)
18 High-kicking dance (6)
19 Prayer ending word (4)
20 In that place (5)
21 Phoney (5)

Down

1 Cut finely (5)
2 Calm central region of a cyclone (3)
3 Supporter of equal rights for women (8)
4 Charge someone with too many tasks (9)
5 Sleazy or shabby (5)
7 Of weapons, designed to reach remote targets (4-5)
9 Sing and play for somebody (8)
11 Droop (3)
13 Clairvoyance (inits) (3)
15 Smooth surface (as of a cut gemstone) (5)
17 North African port and capital city (5)
19 Gone by (3)

148

Across
1 Makes beer (5)
4 Green salad vegetable (5)
7 Imitate (3)
8 Make less visible, obscure (5)
10 Miss Widdecombe, former MP (3)
11 Grape plant (4)
12 Gather into a ruffle (5)
14 Sanctify (5)
15 Aqualung (5)
16 Gangway (5)
19 Roster (4)
20 Coaster (3)
21 Entomb (5)
23 Craft considered to have extraterrestrial origins (inits) (3)
24 Tapestry used as a wall hanging (5)
25 Baby's wear (5)

Down
1 Early form of modern jazz (5)
2 Imp (3)
3 Sign of the zodiac (11)
4 Occasion for festivities to mark a happy event (11)
5 Pencil rubbers (7)
6 Air cavity in the skull (5)
9 Reproductive cells (3)
13 Circle equidistant from the north and south poles (7)
15 Latin American dance (5)
17 Forename of golfer, Mr Woosnam (3)
18 Before due time (5)
22 Piece of advice (3)

149

1		2		3	■	4	5		6	
	■		■		■	■		■		■
7					8	■	9			
	■		■	10				■		■
11			12			■	13			14
	■	■		■		■		■	■	
15	16			■	17	18		19		
■		■	20				■		■	
21				■	22					
■		■		■	■		■		■	
23					■	24				

Across

1 Country, capital Damascus (5)
4 Afghanistan's capital city (5)
7 Intense feeling of love (6)
9 Chief port of Yemen (4)
10 Ripped (4)
11 Drive from behind (6)
13 Swindle (4)
15 Behind schedule (4)
17 US gangster ___ Parker, Clyde Barrow's partner (6)
20 Wash with a mop (4)
21 Capital of Italy (4)
22 Repeat aloud from memory (6)
23 Caribbean country (5)
24 Broad thin piece of paper, used for writing (5)

Down

1 Knife used in dissection (7)
2 Wireless (5)
3 Intense (5)
5 Desert, leave (7)
6 Deplete (3,2)
8 Crosspiece that strengthens the frame of a vehicle and prevents injury in case of overturning (4-3)
12 Gift (7)
14 Abstract part of something (7)
16 Distinctive smell (5)
18 Follows orders (5)
19 Artless (5)

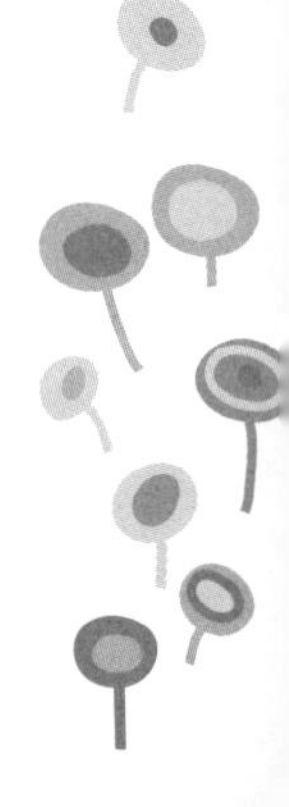

150

Across

1 Displayed (5)

3 Addictive narcotic extracted from poppies (5)

7 State parliament of Russia (4)

9 Chauffeur (6)

10 Succulent plant with spikes of showy flowers (4)

11 Ice cream container (4)

12 Sings the praises of (5)

15 Stony hillside (5)

17 Fish-eating diving duck (4)

19 Keen on (4)

20 Be preoccupied with something (6)

21 Share a boundary (4)

22 Physical strength (5)

23 Fence made of shrubs (5)

Down

1 Entice away from principles or proper conduct (6)

2 Cetacean mammal (5)

4 Thick stew made of rice and chicken (5)

5 Female horse (4)

6 Alpine perennial plant (9)

8 Frenzied (5)

13 Retire from military service (5)

14 Enveloping bandage (6)

16 Minor parish official (5)

17 Platform (5)

18 Potage (4)

151

1	■	2	■	3	■	4		5		6
7							■		■	
	■		■		■		■		■	
8			9		10		11			
	■	■		■		■		■	■	
■	12									■
13	■	■		■		■		■	■	14
15		16		17		18		19		
	■		■		■		■		■	
	■		■	20						
21					■		■		■	

Across

4 Boundary (5)
7 Foment (7)
8 One trained to install, maintain and repair equipment or wiring (11)
12 Absolving from blame (9)
15 Not absolutely essential (11)
20 Frank ___, singer nicknamed Old Blue Eyes (7)
21 Bring together, assemble (5)

Down

1 Enthusiastic (5)
2 Money extracted as a penalty (4)
3 Male red deer (4)
4 Biblical patriarch, Jacob's third son (4)
5 Very short skirt (4)
6 Contaminate (5)
9 Cut thinly (5)
10 Major European river (5)
11 Counters used to represent money when gambling (5)
13 Prompting (5)
14 Little-used side road (5)
16 Group created in 1949 for the purpose of security (inits) (4)
17 Point of the moon, etc (4)
18 Grains on the beach (4)
19 Pretentious (4)

152

Across

1 Buddhist leader who once ruled Tibet (5,4)
8 Ignited again (5)
9 Residence of a clergyman (5)
10 Liturgical vestment worn by priests (3)
11 Peak of a cap (5)
13 Creature with striped legs, related to the giraffe (5)
15 Item of dining room furniture (5)
18 Puts a name to (5)
20 Collection of rules imposed by authority (3)
21 Abrupt (5)
22 Coral reef (5)
23 Play traditionally popular with children at Christmas (9)

Down

2 Collection of maps (5)
3 Communion table (5)
4 West Indian dance (5)
5 Miraculous food (5)
6 Move toward (9)
7 Large mass of land projecting into the sea (9)
12 Lubricant (3)
14 Colourful ornamental carp (3)
16 Mountainous republic in south-eastern Asia (5)
17 Choose by a vote (5)
18 Group of many insects (5)
19 Atmosphere of depression (5)

153

Across

1 Data input device for computers (6)
6 Light-sensitive membrane (6)
7 Plenty (4)
8 Mourn the loss of (6)
10 Artist's tripod (5)
13 Tramp about (7)
16 Gas formerly used as an anaesthetic (5)
18 Player who delivers the ball to the batsman (6)
20 Items used to secure washing to a line (4)
21 Several parallel layers of material (6)
22 ___ dancers, traditionally associated with May Day (6)

Down

1 Ms Minogue (5)
2 Placard (6)
3 Pull, haul (4)
4 Ancient Assyrian city on the Tigris (7)
5 Tall tower referred to in the Bible (5)
9 Cable (4)
11 Attendant on an aeroplane (7)
12 Body of water (4)
14 Dazed state (6)
15 Rotund, extremely chubby (5)
17 Fragrant garden flowers (5)
19 Ramble aimlessly (4)

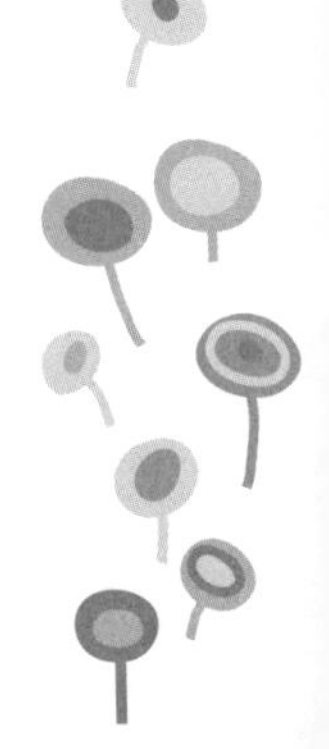

154

Across

1 Turned-back hems at the ends of sleeves (5)
4 Roman god of love (5)
7 Cheap purchase (7)
8 Be in a horizontal position (3)
9 Hindu social class (5)
11 Pieces of potato fried in deep fat or oil (5)
12 Light narrow boat (5)
14 Echo sounder (acronym) (5)
16 Mr Garfunkel, singer-songwriter (3)
17 First book of the Old Testament (7)
19 Number in a trio (5)
20 Saline (5)

Down

1 Three-dimensional (5)
2 Cone-bearing evergreen (3)
3 Have in common (5)
4 Sarcastic pessimist (5)
5 Seat behind the rider of a motorbike (7)
6 Frock (5)
10 US legislator (7)
12 Recite with musical intonation (5)
13 Tidal bore in a river (5)
14 Drops down (5)
15 Impaired in skill by neglect (5)
18 God of the Sun, the equivalent of the Greek god Helios (3)

155

Across

1 Rising upward (9)
8 Native of Baghdad, for example (5)
9 Perform a wedding ceremony (5)
10 Train driver's compartment (3)
11 Moved slowly and stealthily (5)
13 Open and observable (5)
15 Friendship (5)
18 Be superior to (5)
20 Sense organ for hearing (3)
21 Tropical fruit with a yellow skin and pink pulp (5)
22 Mrs Major, wife of former UK prime minister John (5)
23 Dispersed (9)

Down

2 Empty area (5)
3 Expel from one's property (5)
4 Walt Disney film of 1941 (5)
5 Relating to Scandinavia (5)
6 Emit or release a substance (9)
7 Shiite religious leader (9)
12 Domesticated animal kept for companionship (3)
14 Irritate (3)
16 Old Testament patriarch (5)
17 Fungi used as an agent for raising bread dough (5)
18 Premium Bonds computer (5)
19 Marie ___, chemist who discovered radium (5)

156

Across

1 Book for collecting stamps (5)
4 Squeeze with the fingers (5)
7 Nymph who fell in love with Narcissus and faded away, leaving just her voice (4)
9 Cancellation of civil rights (9)
11 Glowering, moody (4)
13 Pacified, placated (8)
15 Gifts (8)
16 Makes a mistake (4)
19 Regions that are dangerous or impossible to enter (2-2,5)
22 Former name of Thailand (4)
23 Light-beam intensifier (5)
24 Fabulous, wonderful! (5)

Down

1 Very dry (4)
2 Dandy (4)
3 Got together (3)
4 Greek letter (3)
5 Arm of the Mediterranean (6,3)
6 King of Judea who ordered the death of many children (5)
8 Girl's name (9)
10 Change the position of (9)
12 Above, beyond (4)
14 Arabian ruler (4)
15 Control board (5)
17 Letters on an invitation to request a response (inits) (4)
18 Disfigurement (4)
20 Ventilate (3)
21 Units used in printing (3)

157

Across

1 Signboard over a shopfront (6)

6 Landlocked African republic (6)

7 Cash register (4)

8 Snuggle (6)

10 Citrus fruit (5)

13 Scottish resort and fishing port (3)

15 Looked at with amorous intentions (5)

18 Lessen the strength of (6)

20 Situated at the top of (4)

21 Verbally report or maintain (6)

22 Guide (6)

Down

1 Bringing death (5)

2 Stringed instrument (5)

3 Prayer ending word (4)

4 Diplomatic (7)

5 Animal with two feet (5)

9 Major monetary unit (4)

11 Amazing or wonderful occurrence (7)

12 Epithet (4)

14 Adjust finely (5)

16 Dutch cheese shaped in a ball (5)

17 Small restaurant (5)

19 Christmas (4)

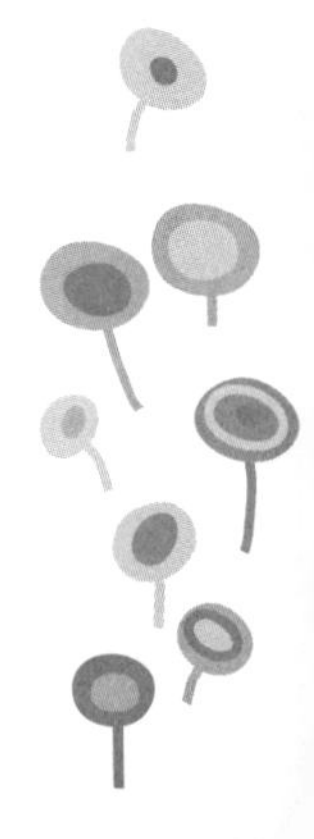

158

Across

1 Resembling an ape (6)
6 Add on, supplement (6)
7 Bullets, etc (abbr) (4)
9 Regions on diametrically opposite sides of the Earth (9)
13 Mood disorder (5)
15 Ancient unit of length (5)
17 Be valid (5)
20 Not marked by the use of reason (9)
23 Identical (4)
24 Shelters from light (6)
25 Most senior (6)

Down

1 Involuntary muscular contraction (5)
2 Relating to a person or thing regarded as a representative symbol (6)
3 Follower of Hitler (4)
4 Expired (4)
5 Probabilities (4)
8 Adult male person (3)
10 Greyish-brown colour (5)
11 Monetary value (5)
12 Garden of Adam and Eve (4)
14 Edge tool used to cut and shape wood (4)
16 Thrown carelessly (6)
18 Large nation (inits) (3)
19 Provide a remedy (5)
20 Neither good nor bad (2-2)
21 Close by (4)
22 Misplace (4)

159

Across

2 Animal that feeds on refuse (9)

6 Worries excessively (5)

7 Measures of land (5)

9 Each and every (3)

10 Appetising (5)

12 Weapon that delivers a temporarily paralysing electric shock (5)

14 Appeal (5)

17 Assert (5)

19 Rod Hull's famous bird (3)

20 Connected with birth (5)

21 Inquired in a meddlesome way (5)

22 Carnival held on Shrove Tuesday (5,4)

Down

1 Metal fastener in the form of a clasp, with a guard (6,3)

2 Oozes (5)

3 Analysis of a substance such as gold or silver, to determine its make-up (5)

4 Glorify (5)

5 Lasses (5)

8 Admit defeat (9)

11 Popular hot beverage (3)

13 Astern (3)

15 Organic compound (5)

16 City in India (5)

17 Excellent (5)

18 Farewell remark (5)

160

Across

1 Discrimination against a person in the latter part of life (6)
6 Place of religious retreat for Hindus (6)
7 Harvested (6)
9 Childhood disease (7)
13 Defence plea of being elsewhere (5)
14 Ms Campbell, model (5)
15 Alcoholic spirit (3)
16 Organic compound (5)
19 Airport in Chicago (5)
20 Painted structures of a stage set (7)
22 Have a lofty goal (6)
23 Illustrious (6)
24 Small gun (6)

Down

1 Medium for radio and television broadcasting (8)
2 Cause to grow thin or weak (8)
3 Manufactured (4)
4 Capital of Tibet (5)
5 Capital of the US state of Oregon (5)
8 Person who leaves one country to settle in another (6)
10 Vexes (6)
11 Fervent supporter of a person or institution (8)
12 Relating to the stars or constellations (8)
17 Scarper (5)
18 Register formally as a participant (5)
21 Coarse file (4)

161

1		2		3	■	4	5		6	
	■		■		■	■		■		■
	■		■	7	8					
9						■		■		■
	■		■	10				11		■
12	13		14	■		■	15			16
■	17					18	■		■	
■		■		■	19					
20							■		■	
■		■		■	■		■		■	
21					■	22				

Across

1 Keyboard instrument (5)
4 Beat, pound (5)
7 Ecstasy (7)
9 Sloping kind of print (6)
10 Without danger (6)
12 Ship's wheel (4)
15 Poorly lit (4)
17 Plant with spiny bracts (6)
19 Mocks up (6)
20 Small dog similar to a greyhound (7)
21 Line spoken by an actor to the audience (5)
22 Aroma (5)

Down

1 Local church community (6)
2 Diffusing warmth and friendliness (7)
3 Fragrant rootstock of various irises (5)
5 Intense dislike (6)
6 One who suffers for the sake of principle (6)
8 Scholarly life (7)
11 Outfit (clothing and accessories) for a new baby (7)
13 Engraves with acid (6)
14 Made a diagrammatic representation of an area (6)
16 In Islam, the will of Allah (6)
18 Egyptian water lily (5)

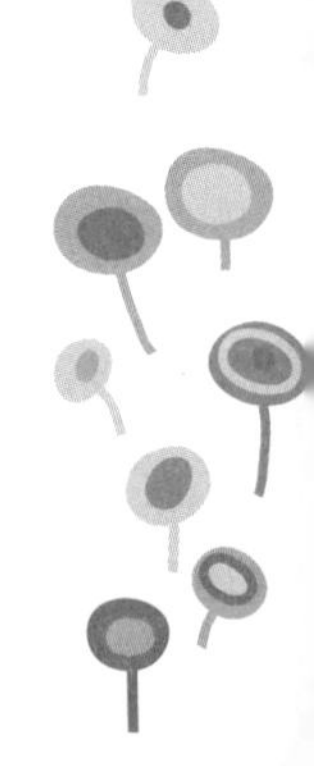

162

Across

1 Capital of Belarus (5)
3 Court game resembling handball (5)
7 Star that ejects material (4)
9 Emotional wound (6)
10 Succulent plant (4)
11 Wheel shaft (4)
12 Dexterous (5)
15 Short line at the end of the main strokes of a character (5)
17 Burrowing mammal (4)
19 Assist in crime (4)
20 Ludicrous acts done for fun (6)
21 Unconscious state (4)
22 Country, capital Kathmandu (5)
23 Emblem (5)

Down

1 Handbook (6)
2 Oil-bearing laminated rock (5)
4 Iconic mental representation (5)
5 Kill (4)
6 Unwavering (9)
8 Device used to control a flow (5)
13 Picture recorded by a camera (abbr) (5)
14 Spoil the appearance of (6)
16 Indian side dish of yogurt and chopped cucumbers (5)
17 Holy city (5)
18 Farm outbuilding (4)

163

Across

1 Upstanding or highborn (5)
3 Labours (5)
7 Walk silently (6)
9 Type of sousaphone (4)
10 Severely punished or reprimanded (10)
14 Tip of an ink pen (3)
16 Document signed by King John in 1215 (5,5)
19 Manufacturer of popular toy bricks (4)
20 Chatter (6)
22 Drying cloth (5)
23 Gush (5)

Down

1 Intimation of dismissal (6)
2 Allow (3)
4 Eight singers who perform together (5)
5 Long-necked bird (4)
6 Large, old, luminous stars (3,6)
8 Civil or military authority in Turkey (5)
11 Hostelry (3)
12 The alphabet (inits) (3)
13 Type of heron (5)
15 Warning or proviso (6)
17 Item worn on the hand (5)
18 Level (4)
21 Pinnacle (3)

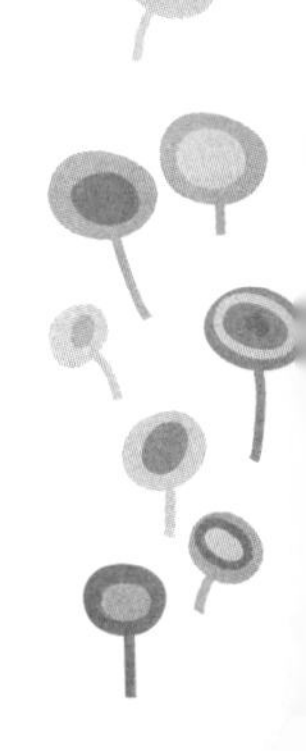

164

Across

1 Collection of things (5)
3 Small plant-sucking insect (5)
7 Vendor (6)
9 Unorthodox or false religion (4)
10 Boat built by Noah (3)
11 Moulders (4)
13 Prune, cut back the growth of (3)
15 Ballroom dance in double time (3-4)
17 Star sign between Cancer and Virgo (3)
18 Floor on a boat (4)
20 Caustic washing solution (3)
21 Opaque gem (4)
22 Cause extensive destruction (6)
24 Act ostentatiously (5)
25 Pitchers (5)

Down

1 Small informal restaurant (6)
2 Pass between mountain peaks (3)
4 Preserved in vinegar (7)
5 Obligation (4)
6 Woman's undergarment (9)
8 Espresso coffee with milk (5)
12 Bloated (7)
14 Form of musical entertainment (5)
16 Those who travel on the piste, for example (6)
19 Domesticated bovine animals (4)
23 Solemn pledge (3)

165

1		2		3		■	4			5
	■		■		■	■		■	■	
	■	6							7	
8	9		■		■	■		■		■
10			11		12	■	13			
■		■	14			15		■		■
16				■	17			18		19
■		■		■	■		■	20		
21									■	
	■	■		■	■		■		■	
22				■	23					

Across

1 Light glass formed on the surface of some lavas (6)
4 Expressed in words (4)
6 Habitual hour for a midday meal (9)
8 Not easily explained (3)
10 Reddish-brown (6)
13 Articulate in a very careful and rhythmic way (4)
14 Instant (5)
16 Hindu meditation and relaxation method (4)
17 Female sibling (6)
20 Complexion (3)
21 Litter used as a means of transporting sick people (9)
22 Cautious (4)
23 Sliding container in a piece of furniture (6)

Down

1 Beforehand (5)
2 Coalesces (5)
3 Malignant growth or tumour (6)
4 Brings to a final conclusion (7)
5 Mature female deer (3)
7 Environmental condition, surroundings (6)
9 Rough dwelling made in a trench (6)
11 Statuesque (7)
12 "It is", poetically (3)
15 Message written in secret code (6)
18 Chuck (5)
19 Happen again (5)
21 Adult female hog (3)

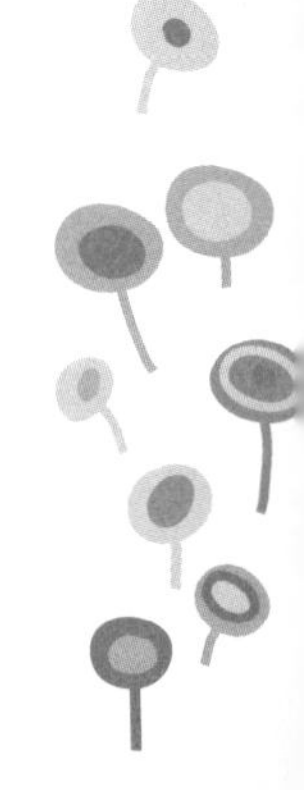

166

1		2		3	■	4		5		6
	■		■		■		■		■	
7			■	8						
	■	9	10		■		■	■	■	
11	12				13		14		15	
■		■		■		■		■		■
16				17		18		19		20
	■	■	■		■	21			■	
22		23					■	24		
	■		■		■		■		■	
25					■	26				

Across

1 Lines made of twisted fibres (5)
4 Strongboxes for valuables (5)
7 Bow (3)
8 Wearing away (7)
9 Foot digit (3)
11 Happening without apparent external cause (11)
16 Shop assistant (11)
21 Auction item (3)
22 With legs stretched far apart (7)
24 Law passed by Parliament (3)
25 First Englishman to circumnavigate the globe (5)
26 Alpine vocal call (5)

Down

1 Talons (5)
2 Right-hand page (5)
3 Item of bed linen (5)
4 Contempt (5)
5 US law enforcement agency (inits) (3)
6 Despatches (5)
10 Erstwhile (4)
12 Leguminous plant (3)
13 Snake (3)
14 Major monetary unit (4)
15 Visitor from space? (inits) (3)
16 Endure, put up with (5)
17 Substance used to flavour food (5)
18 Lament for the dead (5)
19 Sedate, respectable (5)
20 Connected with birth (5)
23 Afternoon meal (3)

Across

1 Cursory (6)
6 Public speaker (6)
7 Dark grey cloud (6)
9 Goddess of retribution (7)
13 Implements used in the practice of a vocation (5)
14 Daisy-like flower (5)
15 Clear (5)
18 Force (5)
19 Non-metallic element (7)
21 Ancient country and place of pilgrimage in south-west Asia on the Mediterranean (6)
22 Point in the sky directly above the observer (6)
23 Swelling from excessive accumulation of fluid (6)

Down

1 Monument built to honour soldiers (8)
2 Final aggregate (3,5)
3 Misplace (4)
4 Gateaux (5)
5 Motion picture (5)
8 Not famous or acclaimed (6)
10 Dock (6)
11 State of inactivity following an interruption (8)
12 Country formerly known as Ceylon (3,5)
16 Crippled (5)
17 Order of Greek architecture (5)
20 Reverberate (4)

168

Across

1 Inhaled the odour of (5)
4 Receptacle for a coin (4)
6 Strong restless desire (4)
8 Jewish spiritual leader (5)
9 Death of part of the living body (8)
12 Antlered animal (4)
13 Drench (5)
15 Unemotional person (5)
17 Descended, came down (4)
19 Become hard, set (8)
21 Dullards (5)
22 Corrode, as with acid (4)
23 Arabian ruler (4)
24 Adjust finely (5)

Down

1 Stitched (4)
2 Derive, evoke (5)
3 Private instructor (5)
4 Flavoured with herbs and spices (8)
5 Two times (5)
7 Network (4)
10 Make changes in text (4)
11 Record book (8)
14 Consciousness of one's own identity (4)
15 Move furtively (5)
16 Expense (4)
17 Conflict (5)
18 Unit of capacity (5)
20 Yellow part of an egg (4)

169

Across

1 Title given to Siddartha Gautama (c563–483BC), founder of a religion (6)
4 Chilly (4)
6 Remove one's email address from a mailing list (11)
8 Bunch of cords fastened at one end (6)
12 Mount ___, the highest peak in Japan (4)
13 Double (5)
15 Female horse (4)
16 Object thrown in athletic competitions (6)
19 Communication sent successively to many people (5,6)
20 Went on horseback (4)
21 Child of an aunt or uncle (6)

Down

1 Having a broad or rounded end (5)
2 Workstations (5)
3 Official language of Israel (6)
4 Open-topped glass flasks used for serving wine or water (7)
5 Owing (3)
7 Small and delicately worked item (5)
9 Swamped with water (5)
10 Aseptic (7)
11 Saucepan cover (3)
14 Roman statesman and orator (6)
17 Makes reference to (5)
18 Device producing a loud sound as a warning (5)
19 Low-breed dog (3)

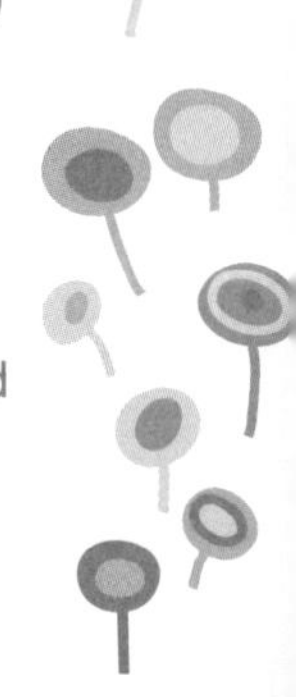

170

1			2		■	3		4		5
	■	■		■	■		■		■	
6					■	7	8			
	■	■		■	9	■		■	■	
10	11								12	
■		■		■		■		■		■
13										14
	■	■		■		■		■	■	
15		16		17	■	18				
	■		■		■	■		■	■	
19					■	20				

Across

1 Detect some circumstance or entity automatically (5)
3 Mythical Greek giant with 100 eyes (5)
6 Brand name (5)
7 Kingdom in the South Pacific (5)
10 Medical instrument for listening to sounds (11)
13 Device used to measure a vehicle's rate of travel (11)
15 Explosion (5)
18 Lagoon encircled by a coral reef (5)
19 Person who acts as host at formal occasions (coll) (5)
20 Place where milk, butter, cheese, etc is produced (5)

Down

1 Garments of a jockey (5)
2 Climbing plants that produce fragrant flowers (9)
3 Liable (3)
4 Alcoholic spirit flavoured with juniper berries (3)
5 Ordered series (5)
8 Musical group (9)
9 Non-metallic element, atomic number 5 (5)
11 Upper part (3)
12 Food wrapped in a pastry shell (3)
13 Animal prized for its fur (5)
14 Pass on (5)
16 Curve (3)
17 One of the digits of the foot (3)

171

Across

1 Island located south of Sicily (5)
3 Provide food (5)
6 Parody (5)
9 Accumulate (5)
10 Car crash (sl) (5)
12 Earth colour (6)
13 Russian emperor (4)
14 Travel in front (4)
15 Length of a line segment between the centre and circumference of a circle (6)
19 Conduit for carrying off waste products (5)
20 Culpability (5)
21 Province of eastern Belgium (5)
22 Pale yellowish to yellowish brown (5)
23 Holy apparition (5)

Down

1 Old Testament prophet (5)
2 Prickle, barb (5)
3 Steep rugged rock or cliff (4)
4 Come about, happen (9)
5 Vertical part of a stair (5)
7 Surgical procedure (9)
8 Device for creating a current of air (3)
11 Mother-of-pearl (5)
14 Former Nigerian capital (5)
16 Pointed tool for marking surfaces (3)
17 Condescend (5)
18 Incantation (5)
19 Remain (4)

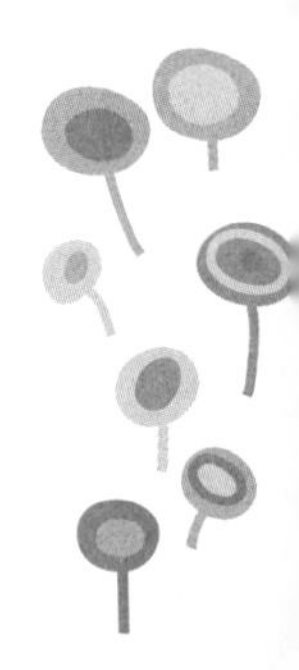

172

Across

1 For, in favour of (3)
3 Bracelets (7)
6 One who pretends to have special knowledge or ability (9)
8 Flightless Australian bird (3)
10 Frozen dessert made with fruit juice (6)
13 Cut-price event (4)
14 Love intensely (5)
16 Release after a security has been paid (4)
17 New Testament book telling the story of Christ (6)
20 Large monkey (3)
21 Attacker (9)
22 Person who receives support and protection from a patron (7)
23 Retired person (inits) (3)

Down

1 Tubes (5)
2 Come about (5)
3 Brought (a vehicle) to a halt (6)
4 Spectacles (7)
5 Male offspring (3)
7 In a slumber (6)
9 Quagmire (6)
11 Weight used to stabilise a ship (7)
12 Duvet warmth rating (3)
15 Go round and round (6)
18 Terrace (5)
19 Become less in amount or intensity (3,2)
21 High mountain (3)

1		2			3		4		5	
					6					
7										
				8		9				
10	11									
12								13		14
								15		
16			17		18					
							19			
20										
					21					

173

Across

1 Frank and direct (6)
6 Person deprived of the protection of the legal system (6)
7 Sullen (4)
8 Animal product used as a furniture polish (7)
10 (They) exist (3)
12 Appropriate to grand and formal occasions (11)
15 Went faster (3)
16 Empty out, exhaust of contents (7)
19 This place (4)
20 Make a forceful request (6)
21 Gradually acquire new traits or characteristics (6)

Down

1 French brandy (6)
2 Gender that refers to inanimate objects (6)
3 Completed (4)
4 Mr Redding who sang *(Sittin' on) The Dock of the Bay* (4)
5 Capital of Nicaragua (7)
8 Dome-shaped dessert (5)
9 Premium Bonds computer (5)
11 Official who is expected to ensure fair play (7)
13 Difficult experience (6)
14 Involuntary expulsion of air from the nose (6)
17 Hinged section of a table (4)
18 Periodic rise and fall of sea level (4)

174

Across

1 Slippery sloping surface in a children's playpark (5)
3 Hidden supply (5)
6 Horse breed (4)
8 Idolised (6)
9 Baby's napkin (3)
11 City in central Japan on southern Honshu (5)
12 Induce (5)
13 Named prior to marriage (3)
14 Two times (5)
15 Sore often found in the mouth (5)
18 Roman god of the Sun (3)
19 Upset, offended (6)
20 Ridge of rock, coral, etc (4)
21 Impurities left in the final drops of a liquid (5)
22 Ms Minogue (5)

Down

1 Light, informal meal (5)
2 Accounting entry recording a sum owed (5)
3 Insignia used by the medical profession (8)
4 Blood cell (9)
5 Empower (5)
7 Native Australian (9)
10 Filleted (8)
14 Moderately warm (5)
16 Large truck (5)
17 Type of firearm (5)

1		2		3	■	4	5		6	
	■		■		■	■		■		■
7					8	■	9			
	■		■	10				■		■
11			12			■	13			14
	■	■		■		■		■	■	
15	16			■	17	18		19		
■		■	20				■		■	
21				■	22					
■		■		■	■		■		■	
23					■	24				

Across

1 Steer clear of (5)
4 Drama set to music (5)
7 Drinking vessel (6)
9 Run competitively (4)
10 Fossil fuel (4)
11 Foundation garment (6)
13 Vegetable known as lady's fingers (4)
15 Dull or stupid person (4)
17 Type of beetle (6)
20 Cultivated land as a unit (4)
21 Stand to support a coffin (4)
22 Over there (6)
23 Traffic light colour (5)
24 Avarice, gluttony (5)

Down

1 Substance taken to counter indigestion (7)
2 Transmitting live from a studio (2,3)
3 The two in a pack of playing cards (5)
5 Sitting room (7)
6 Come back (5)
8 Earthenware (7)
12 Liberate (3,4)
14 Enraged (7)
16 "Religion is the ___ of the people", Karl Marx (5)
18 In the middle of (5)
19 Tapering block (5)

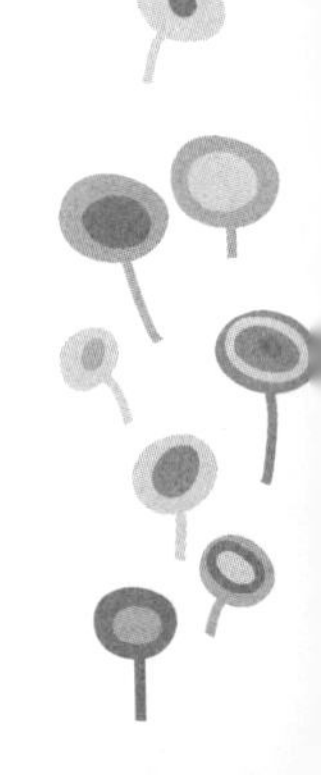

176

Across

1 Thaws (5)
4 Hawaiian greeting (5)
7 Sensation of acute discomfort (4)
9 Paper advancing a new point of view resulting from research (6)
10 Rotate (4)
11 Dull pain (4)
12 British nobleman (4)
15 Speech defect (4)
17 Roman love poet, born in 43 BC (4)
19 Parasite of man (4)
20 Thick and heavy shoe (6)
22 Dainty (4)
23 Monastery (5)
24 Native of Stockholm, for example (5)

Down

1 Cloak (6)
2 Interweave (4)
3 Rich brown pigment (5)
5 Beam over a doorway (6)
6 Overbearing pride or presumption (6)
8 Attribute (7)
13 Great coolness and composure (6)
14 Despise (6)
16 Gratify (6)
18 Clothing (5)
21 Total admission receipts at a sports event (4)

1	■	2	■	3			4		5	
6					■	■		■		■
	■		■	7						
8					■	■		■		■
	■		■	9	10			11		12
13	14		15	■		■	16			
17						18	■		■	
■		■		■	■	19				
20							■		■	
■		■		■	■	21				
22							■		■	

Across

3 Liquorice-flavoured herb (7)
6 Women's quarters (5)
7 Embarrassed (7)
8 Public announcement of a proposed marriage (5)
9 Child's two-wheeled vehicle operated by foot (7)
13 Sound of a bell (4)
16 Nocturnal flying creature (4)
17 Encumber with an overwhelming amount of work (3,4)
19 Loose fibre obtained by untwisting old rope (5)
20 Innovator (7)
21 Look down on with disdain (5)
22 Unwanted discharge of a fluid (7)

Down

1 Stick vegetable, eaten as a fruit (7)
2 Pressing clothes with a heated tool (7)
3 Accumulate (5)
4 Ski race over a winding course (6)
5 Loophole (6)
10 Female of domestic cattle (3)
11 Bun or short ponytail worn on the crown of the head (7)
12 Having corresponding terminal sounds (7)
14 Antiseptic used to treat wounds (6)
15 Port city of northern Poland (6)
18 Norwegian language (5)

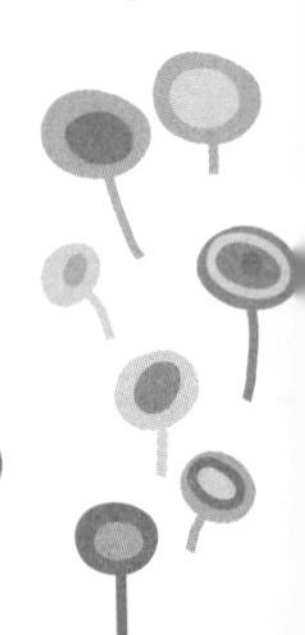

178

Across

1 Casts off, sloughs (5)
5 Uncooked (3)
7 Tagliatelle or ravioli, for example (5)
8 Machine tool (5)
9 Essential oil or perfume obtained from flowers (5)
11 Extreme Liberal (7)
14 Wish harm upon (4)
15 Direct (4)
17 Slanted letters (7)
20 Cause fear in (5)
21 Dry white Italian wine (5)
22 Abrupt (5)
23 Beer (3)
24 River that flows through Kelso (5)

Down

1 Brine-cured (6)
2 Kill on a large scale (11)
3 Swiftness (5)
4 Old Testament patriarch (5)
5 Pit viper with horny segments at the end of the tail (11)
6 Low dam built across a stream (4)
10 Bath powder (4)
12 Opposed (4)
13 Ailing (3)
16 Act against an attack (6)
18 Type of nut, in a cup-shaped base (5)
19 Picture placed within the bounds of a larger one (5)
20 Mountain lion (4)

179

1		2		3	4	■	5			6
	■		■	7				■	■	
	■	8				■	9	10		
11	12		■		■	13	■		■	
■		■	14						15	
16		17	■		■		■	18		
19								■		■
	■		■		■		■	20		21
22			23	■	24				■	
	■	■	25				■		■	
26				■	27					

Across

1 Hired hand who tends cattle (6)
5 Twilight (4)
7 Dandy (4)
8 Direction of the rising sun (4)
9 Framework (4)
11 Boy (3)
14 Distribute according to a plan (8)
16 In favour of (3)
18 Be nosy (3)
19 Response (8)
20 Got together (3)
22 European mountain range (4)
24 Walk through water (4)
25 Surrounded by (4)
26 Back garden (4)
27 Bowl-shaped drinking vessel (6)

Down

1 Tight-fitting hats (4)
2 At what time? (4)
3 No longer in use (8)
4 Nevertheless (3)
5 Excavated (3)
6 Urinary organ (6)
10 Harvest a crop (4)
12 Musical instrument (4)
13 American state in the Rocky Mountains (8)
15 Faithful (4)
16 Monastery (6)
17 Inclined surface (4)
20 Repast (4)
21 Diplomacy (4)
23 Unhappy (3)
24 Synthetic hairpiece (3)

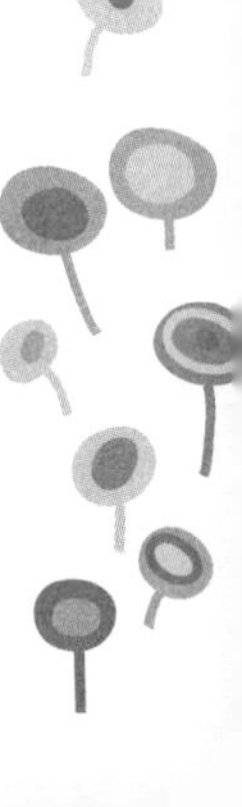

180

1		2		3	■	4	5		6	
	■		■		■	■		■		■
	■		■	7						
8					■	■		■		■
	■		■	9	10			11		12
13	14		15	■		■	16			
17						18	■		■	
■		■		■	■	19				
20							■		■	
■		■		■	■		■		■	
21					■	22				

Across

1 Intense low-pressure weather system (5)

4 Jovial (5)

7 Person who receives support and protection from a patron (7)

8 Derogatory, sneering (5)

9 Leaves in order to join an opposing cause (7)

13 Muslim prayer leader (4)

16 Examine (4)

17 Hues, tints (7)

19 Prostrate (5)

20 Material wealth (7)

21 Brings on to solid food (5)

22 Linger (5)

Down

1 Caused by an earthquake (7)

2 Relating to sight (7)

3 Motorised bicycle (5)

5 Beginning (6)

6 Illuminates (6)

10 Make a mistake (3)

11 Get over an illness (7)

12 Sharply (7)

14 Team spirit (6)

15 Movement (6)

18 Cleave (5)

181

Across

1 South Pacific island group (5)
4 Gather together in large numbers (5)
7 Human-like robot (7)
8 Set burning (3)
9 Fit of temper (coll) (5)
11 Farm with facilities for livestock (5)
12 Dance performed by a group of people in single file (5)
14 In line with a length or direction (5)
16 Nickname of US president Eisenhower (3)
17 Bloated (7)
19 One-hundredths of a pound (5)
20 *A Town like ___*, Nevil Shute novel (5)

Down

1 Token indicating that postal fees have been paid (5)
2 Demented (3)
3 Torment (5)
4 Drink made from fermented apple juice (5)
5 City in central Florida (7)
6 Long, narrow excavation in the earth (5)
10 Castle cellar (7)
12 Pleasantly cold and invigorating (5)
13 Passage between rows of seats (5)
14 Fragrance (5)
15 Spirit traditionally imprisoned within a bottle or oil lamp (5)
18 Hawaiian garland of flowers (3)

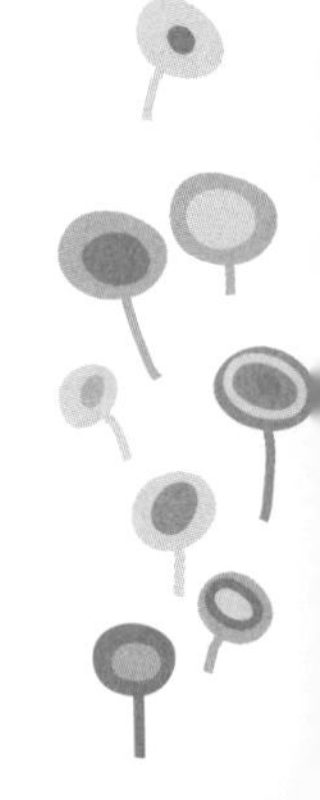

182

Across

1 Phases (6)
6 March aggressively into another's territory (6)
7 Follower of Hitler (4)
8 Former monetary unit of Portugal (6)
10 Japanese rice dish (5)
13 Spear with a shaft and barbed point for throwing (7)
16 Church instrument (5)
18 Countries of Asia (6)
20 Scottish island, capital Portree (4)
21 Perspires (6)
22 In a warm-hearted or gentle manner (6)

Down

1 Air cavity in the skull (5)
2 Japanese woman trained to entertain men (6)
3 One of a series of graduated measurements (as of clothing) (4)
4 Estimating the worth of (7)
5 Snake poison (5)
9 Expression used to frighten away animals (4)
11 Wither, especially due to loss of moisture (7)
12 Metallic element, symbol Fe (4)
14 Communion (6)
15 Typical dwelling-place (5)
17 Destitute (5)
19 Job (4)

183

1			2		■	3	4	5		6
	■	■		■	7				■	
8					■	9				
	■	■		■	10	■		■	■	
11	12								13	
■		■		■		■		■		■
14										15
	■	■		■		■		■	■	
16		17		18	■	19				
	■	20				■		■	■	
21					■	22				

Across

1 Cut-price events (5)

3 Make a mess of (5)

7 Former unit of money in Italy (4)

8 Distinguish oneself (5)

9 Superior grade of black tea (5)

11 False or misleading clues in a mystery (3,8)

14 Capital of Argentina (6,5)

16 Fanatical (5)

19 Highland Games pole (5)

20 By an unknown author, in short (4)

21 Poplar tree (5)

22 Regenerate (5)

Down

1 Long pointed weapon (5)

2 Huge and bulky (11)

3 Small drink (3)

4 Fall from clouds (11)

5 Producer of acorns (3)

6 City on the River Aire (5)

10 Remove by rubbing (5)

12 ___ de Cologne, perfume (3)

13 Word of surprise (3)

14 Loose garment covering the whole body from head to feet (5)

15 Small insectivorous mammal (5)

17 Small roll of soft bread (3)

18 Teacher at a university (3)

184

Across

1 Excellent (5)
4 Workstations (5)
7 Dehydrating, boiling away (11)
8 Cold-blooded creature with a short squat body (4)
11 Lifts up (6)
14 Arrangement (6)
17 Blow delivered with an open hand (4)
21 Providing knowledge (11)
22 Went down on the knees (5)
23 Orders in a particular direction (5)

Down

1 Horizontal support (5)
2 Stringed instrument (5)
3 Uproar, disturbance of the peace (4)
4 Plays, theatre (5)
5 Travels by boat (5)
6 Notices on public display (5)
9 Beam of light (3)
10 Acquire (3)
11 Force by impact (3)
12 Of a thing (3)
13 Epoch, age (3)
14 Arab chief (5)
15 Condiment (5)
16 Precise (5)
18 Fabric made from flax (5)
19 Inner surfaces of the hands (5)
20 Directs a weapon (4)

185

Across

1 Gardening tool (3)
3 Peace and quiet (7)
6 Able to speak two languages fluently (9)
8 *Much ___ about Nothing*, Shakespeare play (3)
10 Light tanker for supplying water or fuel (6)
13 Rare gas (4)
14 Asinine (5)
16 Quiet, serene (4)
17 Ring for sealing a pipe joint (6)
20 Of a female (3)
21 Absence of pain without loss of consciousness (9)
22 Wife of a Russian monarch (7)
23 Gelid (3)

Down

1 Headscarf worn by Muslim women (5)
2 Arm joint (5)
3 Gloomily angry and silent (6)
4 Motors (7)
5 Snake-like fish (3)
7 Point in orbit (6)
9 Realm (6)
11 Alike (7)
12 Boisterous practical joke (3)
15 Sickness (6)
18 Military fabric (5)
19 In sincerity (5)
21 Fitting (3)

186

Across

1 Short sleep (6)

6 Stopped (6)

7 Place end to end without overlapping (4)

8 Own (7)

12 Toxic form of oxygen (5)

13 Film props and scenery (3)

14 ___ Baba (3)

15 And not (3)

17 Step (5)

18 Localised sore (7)

21 Capital of the Maldives (4)

22 Bodyguard (6)

23 Quantity much larger than is needed (6)

Down

1 Legal summons (8)

2 In the open air (8)

3 Resound (4)

4 Heating elements in an electric fire (4)

5 Closely crowded together (5)

8 Silence (5)

9 Natives of Bern, for example (5)

10 Mischievous adventure (8)

11 First courses (8)

16 Corpulent (5)

19 Cut with an axe (4)

20 Location (4)

■	1	2		3		4		5		■
6	■		■		■		■		■	7
8					■	9				
	■		■	10			■		■	
11			12		■	13	14			
	■	■		■	■	■		■	■	
15		16		17	■	18		19		
	■		■	20			■		■	
21					■	22				
	■		■		■		■		■	
■	23									■

Across

1 Scholars (9)
8 Documents showing the legal right to possess a property (5)
9 Grovel (5)
10 Ms Herzigova, supermodel (3)
11 In front (5)
13 Large sea (5)
15 Native-born Israeli (5)
18 Joint of the leg (5)
20 Judo level (3)
21 Semi-precious stone (5)
22 Wine-making fruit (5)
23 Having no real value (9)

Down

2 Light, thin fabric with a wrinkled surface (5)
3 Drugged (5)
4 Former Portuguese province in China (5)
5 Discontinue (5)
6 Latin phrase: done so often that it has become tiresome (2,7)
7 Made an injurious oral statement against a person (9)
12 Ventilate (3)
14 Metal container (3)
16 Great feast (5)
17 Dexterous (5)
18 Person of exceptional holiness (5)
19 English Romantic poet (1795–1821) (5)

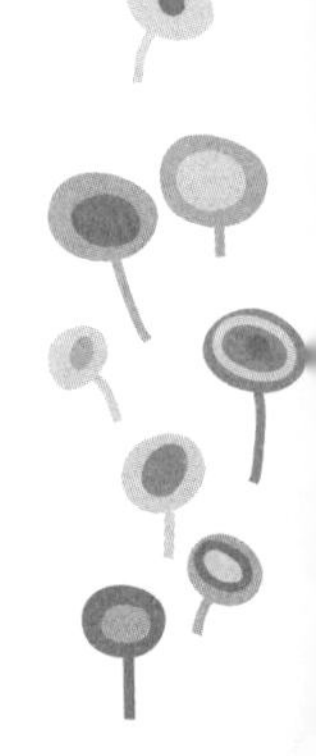

188

Across

4 Young person (5)
7 Arthur ___, former UK Prime Minister (1902–5) (7)
8 Mrs John Major (5)
10 Accuse of being responsible (5)
12 School of whales (3)
13 Of a triangle, having two sides of equal length (9)
17 Word indicating a negative answer (3)
19 ___ Pan, character created by J M Barrie (5)
22 Smell (5)
23 Belonging to another country (7)
24 Sir Francis ___, English sailor (1540–96) (5)

Down

1 Wood used to make piano keys (5)
2 Drinks with a loud sucking noise (6)
3 Wandering tribesmen (6)
4 Baby's bed (4)
5 Ancient Peruvian (4)
6 Continental quilt (5)
9 Sir Patrick ___, famous astronomer (5)
11 Fragrant bushy plant (5)
14 Make certain (6)
15 Protective fold of skin (6)
16 Greenfly, for instance (5)
18 Make amends (5)
20 Loose outer garment worn by Ancient Romans (4)
21 Overabundant (4)

189

Across

1 Sudden and vivid memory of an event in the past (9)

8 Approximately (especially of a date) (5)

9 Clumsy, ill-chosen (5)

10 Animal trap (3)

11 Call to mind (5)

13 Bring out an official document (5)

15 Spring-flowering plant (5)

18 Long seat for more than one person (5)

20 Australian running bird (3)

21 Moves along quickly (5)

22 Sing partly falsetto (5)

23 Supplies, stockpiles (9)

Down

2 *Key* ___, 1948 film (5)

3 Platform (5)

4 Russian pancake (5)

5 Confusion, disarray (5)

6 Chemist or physicist, for example (9)

7 One's partner in marriage (coll) (5,4)

12 Colourful ornamental fish (3)

14 Perceive by sight (3)

16 Insect parasitic on warm-blooded animals (5)

17 Sauce typically served with Italian food (5)

18 Purchaser (5)

19 Prod (5)

190

Across

1 In golf, a hole played in two strokes under par (5)
4 Study intensively, as before an exam (coll) (3,2)
8 Group noun for larks (4)
9 Show to be false (6)
10 Put in (3)
11 Chimney-pot cover (4)
13 Three-dimensional shape (4)
14 Immortal (7)
15 In a competent manner (4)
16 Drink of fermented honey and water (4)
17 High mountain (3)
18 Naval flag (6)
19 Bonnet (4)
21 Revolving arm of a distributor (5)
22 Shed tears (5)

Down

2 Mimic (3)
3 Allegiance (7)
5 Tiny grain, of sugar for instance (7)
6 Professed falsely or insincerely (9)
7 Acting in a secret or dishonest way (9)
8 Pirate (9)
12 Solidly fixed or arranged (4-3)
13 Tree resin used in making mothballs (7)
20 Lyrical poem (3)

191

1			2	■	■	3		4		5
	■	■	6				■		■	
7		8		■	■		■	9		
	■	10		11					■	
12			■		■		■	13		
■	■	14							■	■
15			■		■		■	16		17
	■	18					19		■	
20			■		■	■	21			
	■		■	22				■	■	
23					■	■	24			

Across

1 Adhesive substance (4)
3 Drive out (5)
6 British county dissolved in 1996 (4)
7 Bloc (4)
9 Deciduous tree (3)
10 Novelty (7)
12 ___ and don'ts, rules of behaviour (3)
13 Offence (3)
14 Forgives (7)
15 Expire (3)
16 Label (3)
18 French castle (7)
20 Choose (3)
21 Graven image (4)
22 Incline (4)
23 Convivial gathering (5)
24 Kill intentionally (4)

Down

1 Impressive in scale (5)
2 Facilitate (4)
3 Container for a letter (8)
4 Fastener used on clothing (5,4)
5 Yellow citrus fruit (5)
8 High-ranking police officer (9)
11 Guarantee (8)
15 Wilt (5)
17 Ravine (5)
19 Comes to the assistance of (4)

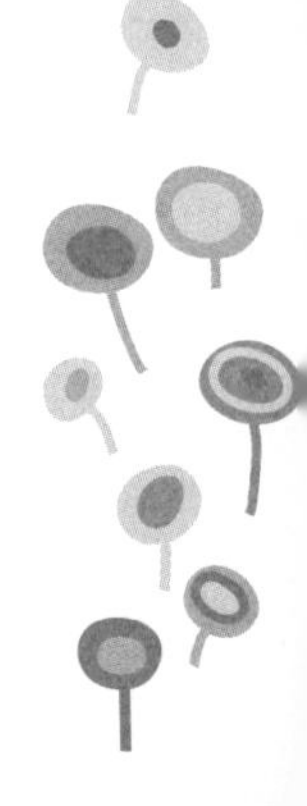

192

Across

1 Tray for serving food or drinks (6)

6 To the opposite side (6)

7 Calculating machine (6)

8 Central American canal (6)

10 Shinbone (5)

13 Strive to equal or match (7)

16 Detector used to locate distant objects (5)

18 Schedule (6)

20 Swelling of the big toe (6)

21 On the move (6)

22 Small rowing boat (6)

Down

1 Aggressive remark directed at a person like a missile (5)

2 Person who is tricked or swindled (6)

3 Coarse file with sharp pointed projections (4)

4 Discovered the site of (7)

5 Commonly encountered (5)

9 Distant (4)

11 At a lower place (7)

12 ___ *Lang Syne*, Scottish song (4)

14 Substance found in tea (6)

15 Trite (5)

17 Fluid (5)

19 In one's sleeping place (4)

193

Across

1 Short-lived (5)
4 Bounder (3)
6 Fluid said to flow in the veins of the gods (5)
7 Child's magazine (5)
9 Group containing one or more species (5)
10 Nobleman (in various countries) ranking above a count (7)
12 Person who cuts and sets panes into windows or doors (7)
14 Finely chopped meat (5)
15 Group of elite soldiers (1-4)
16 Traveller who uses runners to cross snow (5)
17 Collection (3)
18 Sends by post (5)

Down

1 Turned into (6)
2 Lightweight triangular scarf (5)
3 Violent young criminals (5)
4 Long skirt stiffened with hoops (9)
5 Platform (4)
8 Confused multitude of things (5-4)
11 Small pieces of cake, for example (6)
12 Freezing, glacial (5)
13 Panic (5)
14 Fail to hit (4)

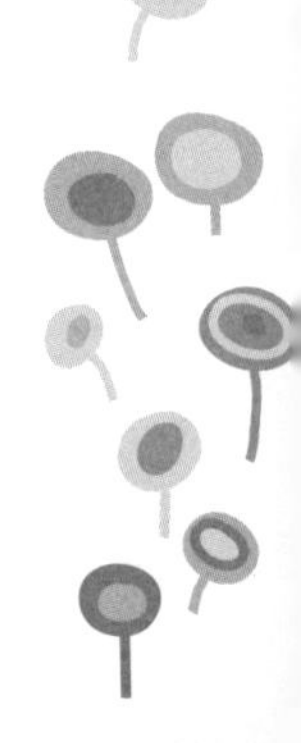

194

Across

1 Russian country house (5)
3 Fill quickly beyond capacity (5)
7 Heavy open wagon (4)
9 Devon city (6)
10 Mound (4)
11 Post (4)
12 Muster strength for a renewed effort (5)
15 Stoppers for bottles, etc (5)
17 Be idle (4)
19 Large bodies of water (4)
20 Retaliate (6)
21 Forcibly pulled apart (4)
22 Mythological beauty, ___ of Troy (5)
23 Legend (5)

Down

1 Flee (6)
2 Luxurious lodging place (5)
4 Circular frame with spokes (5)
5 Airborne soldier (abbr) (4)
6 Unhappy (9)
8 Powerful herbivore with a horned snout (abbr) (5)
13 Hire (5)
14 Take up residence (6)
16 Kitchen appliance used for cooking food (5)
17 Insect grub (5)
18 Hard currency (4)

195

1			2	■	■	3		4		5
	■	■	6				■		■	
7		8		■	■		■		■	
	■	9		10					11	
12	13		■		■		■	14		
■	15									■
16			■		■		■	17		18
19							20		■	
	■		■		■	■	21			
	■		■	22				■	■	
23					■	■	24			

Across

1 Cousin's mother (4)
3 Was gloomy or apathetic (5)
6 Fruit, a cross between a tangerine and a grapefruit (4)
7 Awkward stupid person (4)
9 Stupid or foolish person (coll) (9)
12 Having negative qualities (3)
14 Division of a week (3)
15 Roman soldier (9)
16 Cone-bearing evergreen (3)
17 Mesh (3)
19 Department in charge of the navy (9)
21 Portent (4)
22 Soap froth (4)
23 Grows from, originates (5)
24 Condiment, sodium chloride (4)

Down

1 Remark made spontaneously (2-3)
2 Ballet dancer's skirt (4)
3 Singer of folk songs, troubadour (8)
4 False name (9)
5 Wheeled support on which a camera can be mounted (5)
8 Counteract, sabotage (9)
10 Large case of strong fabric for sleeping on (8)
11 Country road (4)
13 Corrosive compound (4)
16 Is unsuccessful in achieving a goal (5)
18 Religious doctrine proclaimed as true (5)
20 Lob, pitch (4)

196

Across

1 Passes the tongue over (5)
4 Blossom (5)
7 Measure (6)
9 Not this! (4)
11 Utensil with sharp perforations for shredding foods (6)
12 Tenant (6)
14 Large container for liquids (4)
16 Brass instrument (4)
19 Canine film star (6)
22 Sale in small quantities (6)
23 Presidential assistant (4)
24 Tranquillise (6)
25 Samuel ___, English diarist (1633–1703) (5)
26 Burglary (5)

Down

1 Brochure (7)
2 Harvests (5)
3 Sear (5)
5 Mail (7)
6 Airport in Chicago (5)
8 Latticework used to support climbing plants (7)
10 Chop with an axe (3)
13 Statuesque (7)
15 Vote back into office (2-5)
17 Bodily waste water (5)
18 Sleeping place (3)
20 Awake (5)
21 Travel on ice (5)

197

Across

1 Area, zone (6)
6 African country (6)
7 Quantity of paper equal to 500 sheets (4)
8 Fit or worthy to be chosen (8)
11 Double-reed instrument (7)
14 Short-tailed burrowing rodent (7)
18 Go beyond, transgress (8)
19 Bring up (4)
20 Disease of the skin (6)
21 Country, capital Stockholm (6)

Down

1 Scour (5)
2 Multiplication (5)
3 Wireless (5)
4 Man's close-fitting jacket, worn during the Renaissance (7)
5 Bread maker (5)
9 Lakes in Scotland (5)
10 Popular garden ornament (5)
12 Cuddle, embrace tightly (7)
13 One stroke over par in golf (5)
15 Titan forced by Zeus to bear the sky on his shoulders (5)
16 Brief fling of unrestrained spending (5)
17 Repeat performance (5)

198

Across

1 Small natural hollow in the cheek or chin (6)
4 School period (4)
6 Discipline in personal and social activities (9)
8 On a former occasion, poetically (3)
10 Female sibling (6)
13 Pal, chum (4)
14 Angry (5)
16 Shed tears (4)
17 Mattress filled with straw (6)
20 Period of time (3)
21 Kind of gelatin used in making jellies (9)
22 Long narrative poem (4)
23 Extreme mental retardation (6)

Down

1 Hemispherical roofs (5)
2 Adult female horses (5)
3 Smaller in amount (6)
4 Restraint that confines freedom (7)
5 Rug (3)
7 Asian spice (6)
9 Reaches maturity (6)
11 Ill-fated liner (7)
12 Gentle blow (3)
15 Sleeveless jerkin (6)
18 Lariat (5)
19 Toy bear (5)
21 Coat a cake with sugar (3)

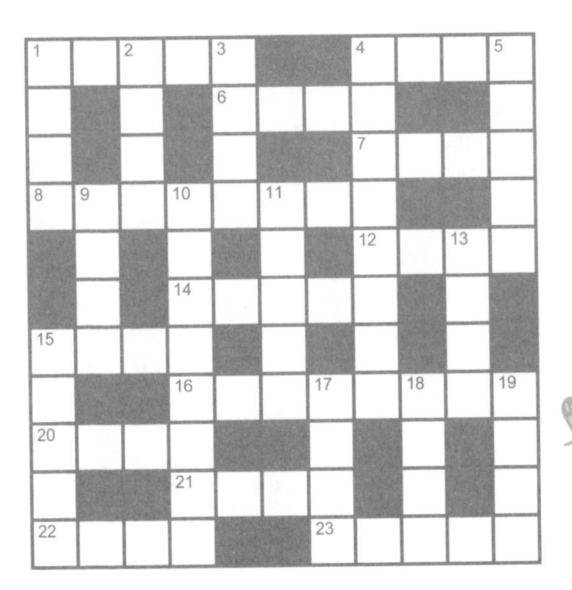

199

Across

1 Earnings (5)
4 Smut from a fire (4)
6 Remove (4)
7 Fourth wife of Henry VIII, ___ of Cleves (4)
8 State of total disorder (8)
12 Part of the body containing the brain (4)
14 Detect some circumstance or entity automatically (5)
15 Division of a dollar (4)
16 Firm in purpose or belief (8)
20 Brink (4)
21 Neuter (a female cat, for example) (4)
22 Digits of the foot (4)
23 Noble gas (5)

Down

1 Sufferings, troubles (4)
2 Mentally or physically infirm with age (4)
3 Pierce with a sharp instrument (4)
4 Outer casing of a marine organism (8)
5 Grooved surface of a pneumatic tyre (5)
9 Flexible pipe for conveying a liquid (4)
10 Kept woman (8)
11 Connecting parts of a chain (5)
13 Assist in crime (4)
15 Swindle (5)
17 Variety of agate (4)
18 Situated at the top of (4)
19 Garden of Adam and Eve (4)

200

Across

1 Fundamental (5)
4 Overhead (5)
7 Military strength (9)
9 Excessive nasality in speech (5)
10 Daily written record of events (5)
12 Otherwise (4)
14 Strap with a crosspiece on the upper of a shoe (1-3)
16 Large evergreen coniferous tree (5)
18 Guitar-like instrument (5)
20 Vertical tube connecting a temporary tap to the mains water supply (9)
21 East African country (5)
22 Go in (5)

Down

1 Conflict (6)
2 Seat for more than one person (4)
3 Breed of long-bodied, short-legged dog (5)
5 Mine disguised as a harmless object (5-4)
6 Capital of Austria (6)
8 Unbecoming or outrageous conduct (9)
11 As well as (3)
13 Sheen (6)
15 Member of a crowd causing a violent disturbance of the peace (6)
17 Endure (5)
19 Clean or orderly (4)

201

Across

1 Design made of small pieces of coloured stone (6)
7 Porch along the outside of a building (7)
8 One who voluntarily suffers death (6)
9 Bicycle for two riders (6)
10 Dried-up riverbed (4)
12 Afflicts (4)
14 Move in large numbers (4)
17 Press and smooth clothing (4)
18 Medical centre (6)
19 Have a lofty goal (6)
21 Measuring instrument consisting of a graduated glass tube (7)
22 Apart from (6)

Down

1 Yellow-flowered tropical tree (6)
2 Scribble (6)
3 Clinging plant (3)
4 Document of credentials (11)
5 Small dynamo with a secondary winding (7)
6 Resist separation (6)
11 Into pieces (7)
13 Decorated the surface of by inserting wood, etc (6)
15 Herb with leaves valued as salad greens (6)
16 Self-effacing (6)
20 Either of male or female (3)

202

Across

1 Mineral used as an abrasive (5)

3 Deadly (5)

7 Residential district, often run-down (6)

9 Musical work (4)

10 Merchandise for sale at a low price in order to draw customers (4-6)

14 Recede (3)

16 Payment (10)

19 Cooing bird (4)

20 Protein that acts as a catalyst (6)

22 Mixture of rain and snow (5)

23 Secret agents (5)

Down

1 Swallow up (6)

2 Long-tailed rodent (3)

4 Audibly (5)

5 Concluding (4)

6 Common affliction, known medically as epistaxis (9)

8 Result from (5)

11 Gave permission to (3)

12 Shortened forename of US president Lincoln (3)

13 Each one, without exception (5)

15 Emphasise (6)

17 Particular items (5)

18 Probabilities (4)

21 Slide fastener (3)

1			2		■	3		4		5
	■	■		■	■		■		■	
6					■		■	7		
	■	■		■	8				■	
9	10			11			■	12	13	
■		■	■	14			■	■		■
15		16	■	17			18			19
	■	20				■		■	■	
21			■		■	22				
	■		■		■	■		■	■	
23					■	24				

Across

1 Contort (5)
3 Long, narrow hill (5)
6 Piece of absorbent cloth (5)
7 Insect (3)
8 Linear units (4)
9 Edible crustacean (7)
12 Posed for artistic purposes (3)
14 Affirmative word (3)
15 Stitch (3)
17 Begged earnestly (7)
20 Centre around which something rotates (4)
21 Saucepan cover (3)
22 Warms up (5)
23 Relating to sea movements (5)
24 Things (5)

Down

1 Absolute (5)
2 Appears to be (5)
3 Go backwards (7)
4 Financial obligations (5)
5 Occurrence (5)
8 Perceives by touch (5)
10 Metal-bearing mineral (3)
11 Representative (7)
13 Unit of surface area equal to 100 square metres (3)
15 Fragmented (5)
16 Walked through water (5)
18 Broker (5)
19 Computer storage items (5)

204

Across

1 Determined in advance (6)

6 Receive (6)

8 Betrayer of one's country (7)

9 Tried out (6)

10 Style, flair (7)

13 Everything (3)

14 Menagerie (3)

17 Homer's epic poem (7)

20 One half of a quarter (6)

21 Exclamation of praise to God (7)

22 Thin slice of meat (especially veal) (6)

23 Native of Mumbai, for example (6)

Down

1 Provide with board and lodging (3,2)

2 Of the backbone (6)

3 Biting tool (5)

4 Designs on the skin (7)

5 Battery terminal (5)

7 Fresh and animated (6)

11 Badly behaved (7)

12 Fit out with garments (6)

15 Sir ___ Mosley (1896–1980), founder of the British Union of Fascists (6)

16 Downy juicy fruit (5)

18 Long loincloth worn by Hindu men (5)

19 Desire strongly or persistently (5)

205

Across

1 Small hut from which newspapers are sold (5)
3 Dance moves (5)
6 Uncommon (4)
8 Cooking in an oven (6)
10 Devotional watch (5)
12 Adipose (5)
14 Form a mental picture (7)
15 Breathes noisily, as if exhausted (5)
16 Church council (5)
18 Sluggish (6)
19 US city known for gambling casinos and easy divorce (4)
20 Return punch (especially by a boxer) (5)
21 Roman goddess of love (5)

Down

1 Russian city on the Vyatka River (5)
2 That girl (3)
3 Five-armed sea creature (8)
4 Being (9)
5 Hanging loosely (5)
7 Record-keeper (9)
9 Arrange or order by categories (8)
11 Little rascal (3)
13 Whatsoever (3)
15 Arise (3,2)
17 Worthless material (5)
19 Regret (3)

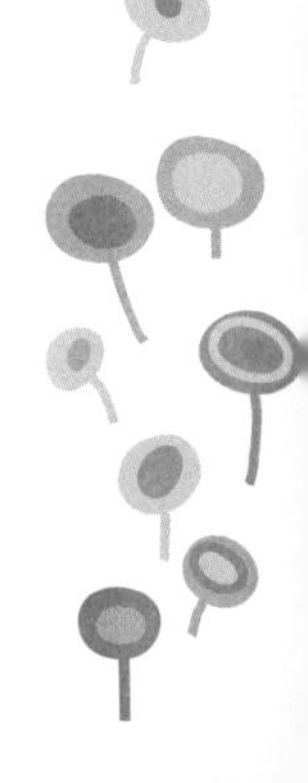

206

Across

1 Capital of Tibet (5)
4 One more time (5)
7 Relieve from (3)
8 Allege (5)
9 Eightsome (5)
10 Listening organ (3)
11 Outmoded (5)
14 Foxhole (5)
17 Cut finely (5)
20 Rascal (5)
23 Yes (3)
24 Boredom (5)
25 Great coolness and composure under strain (5)
26 Bathing resort (3)
27 Cher's former singing partner (5)
28 Inventories (5)

Down

1 Rational (5)
2 Make suitable for a new purpose (5)
3 Having weapons (5)
4 Love intensely (5)
5 Role player (5)
6 Nick (5)
12 Burned remains (3)
13 Stretch (3)
15 Joan of ___, French heroine (3)
16 Male cat (3)
17 Goes in search of (5)
18 Angry dispute (3-2)
19 Lawn flower (5)
20 Floral leaf (5)
21 Zodiacal constellation (5)
22 Machine used for printing (5)

207

Across

1 Threaded (6)

6 Confront, solicit (6)

8 Mound made by social insects (3-4)

9 Charge with carbon dioxide, so as to produce effervescence (6)

10 Cunning (5)

13 Extremely poisonous substance (7)

16 Army unit of two or more divisions (5)

18 Piercingly high-pitched (6)

20 Most uncanny (7)

21 Catch fire (6)

22 Begin again, as with negotiations (6)

Down

1 Waved to and fro (5)

2 Not hallowed or consecrated (6)

3 Fête (4)

4 Widow woman (7)

5 Ready (oneself) for something difficult or unpleasant (5)

7 Priest or religious leader (6)

11 Area for skating (3,4)

12 Young bird of prey (6)

14 Rectangular, dotted playing piece (6)

15 Jelly based on fish or meat stock (5)

17 Smooth fabric (5)

19 Sneering look (4)

208

1		2		3	■	4		5		6
	■		■		■		■		■	
7							■	8		
	■	■	■		■		■		■	
9		10			■	11				
■	■		■	■	■	■	■		■	■
12				13	■	14				15
	■		■		■		■	■	■	
16			■	17				18		
	■		■		■		■		■	
19					■	20				

Across

1 Black bird (5)
4 Striped cat (5)
7 Dressing for a wound (7)
8 Lip (3)
9 Exhales audibly (5)
11 Witty remark (5)
12 Secreting organ in animals (5)
14 Ampoules (5)
16 Put a stop to (3)
17 Inner whorl of petals in a flower (7)
19 Ringo ___, former Beatle (5)
20 Deserving of a scratch (5)

Down

1 Picture puzzle (5)
2 Type of vehicle (3)
3 Draws nigh (5)
4 Time of life between the ages of 13 and 19 (5)
5 Largest anthropoid ape (7)
6 Card game (5)
10 Mother's mother (7)
12 Conjecture (5)
13 Interior furnishings (5)
14 Italian operatic composer (1813–1901) (5)
15 Covered with lather (5)
18 Resin-like substance secreted by certain insects (3)

209

1			2	3	■	4		5		6
	■	■	7		8		■		■	
9										
	■	■		■		■	■		■	
10		11				■	12			
■	■		■	■		■	■		■	■
13				■	14		15			16
	■		■	■		■		■	■	
17				18		19				
	■		■	20				■	■	
21					■	22				

Across

1 Religious doctrine (5)
4 Polite (5)
7 Neither good nor bad (2-2)
9 Happiness (11)
10 Hooded waterproof jacket (6)
12 At another time (4)
13 Savoury meat paste (4)
14 Archer (6)
17 Member of the working class (11)
20 Airhole (4)
21 Twilled woollen fabric (5)
22 Prickle, barb (5)

Down

1 Bedtime drink (5)
2 Organic compound (5)
3 Mature female deer (3)
4 Baby's bed (3)
5 Communist state in Indo-China (7)
6 Language of the Romans (5)
8 Drink, a mixture of lager and cider (9)
11 Located in the open air (7)
13 Conduits used to convey liquids or gases (5)
15 Value (5)
16 Fine strong silky fabric (5)
18 Adam's wife (3)
19 Little insect (3)

210

Across

2 Blood product providing immunity to a disease (9)

6 Like (5)

7 Desert watering hole (5)

9 Mark or flaw (3)

10 Person excessively concerned about propriety and decorum (5)

12 Artist's tripod (5)

14 Mode of expression (5)

17 Ardent follower and admirer (5)

19 Notice of intent to pay (inits) (3)

20 Twist of hair (5)

21 Ringlets (5)

22 Come between so as to be a hindrance (9)

Down

1 Mental position from which things are perceived (9)

2 Former province of western France, on the Loire (5)

3 Common herb (5)

4 Blasphemed (5)

5 Takes a chance (5)

8 Pathological hardening or thickening of tissue (9)

11 Twosome (3)

13 In the past (3)

15 Chemically inactive (5)

16 Mean person (5)

17 Informal term for money (5)

18 Poetry (5)

211

Across

1 Engine (5)

5 Command (3)

7 One who behaves affectedly in order to impress others (6)

8 Right-hand page of a book (5)

10 Knave (5)

11 Free pardon (7)

14 Not yet attempted (7)

16 Sophia ___, Italian film actress (5)

17 Restrains (5)

19 Regional slang (6)

20 Placed (3)

21 Projection shaped to fit into a mortise (5)

Down

1 Capable of causing death (6)

2 Select as an alternative (3)

3 Colloquial term for one's ancestry (5)

4 Type of boat used to transport people and cars (5)

5 Army officer rank (9)

6 Measure of medicine (4)

9 Person drafted into military service (9)

12 Light brown (3)

13 Thomas ___, US inventor (1847–1931) (6)

14 Oneness (5)

15 Implied (5)

16 Wilted (4)

18 Expend (3)

212

1			2		■	3		4		5
	■	■		■	■		■		■	
6					■	7	8			
	■	■		■	9	■		■	■	
10	11								12	
■		■		■		■		■		■
13										14
	■	■		■		■		■	■	
15		16		17	■	18				
	■		■		■	■		■	■	
19					■	20				

Across

1 Smelling of mould (5)
3 Horde (5)
6 Pass out (5)
7 Groom with elaborate care (5)
10 Atheistic, ungodly (11)
13 Tribal healer (8,3)
15 Jolly ___, pirates' flag (5)
18 Round objects used in games (5)
19 Type of firework (5)
20 Of great weight, hefty (5)

Down

1 Civilian dress worn by a military person (5)
2 Small orange (9)
3 Plant fluid (3)
4 Overwhelming feeling of wonder (3)
5 Repairs (5)
8 Say again (9)
9 Belonging to a city (5)
11 Fish eggs (3)
12 Ms Thurman, Hollywood actress (3)
13 Distinguishing features (5)
14 Offensive (5)
16 Wildebeest (3)
17 Steal (3)

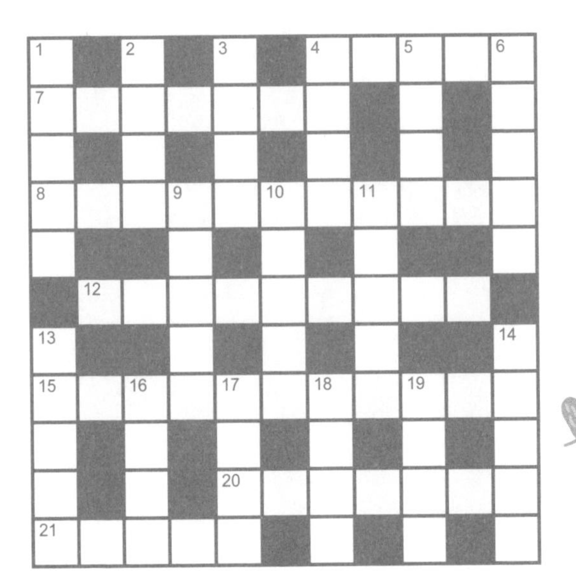

213

Across

4 Lost moisture (5)
7 Pear-shaped fruit (7)
8 Fortune-teller's globe (7,4)
12 Offensive breath (9)
15 Weapon designed to be thrown (4,7)
20 Powered conveyance that carries people up a mountain (3,4)
21 Provide a remedy (5)

Down

1 Piece of cloth used to mend a hole (5)
2 Imitate (4)
3 Lure (4)
4 Child's toy (4)
5 Approximation of quantity, degree or worth (4)
6 Business transactions (5)
9 Dish often eaten in summer (5)
10 Communion table (5)
11 Large wild ox with shaggy hair and a fatty hump (5)
13 Recite with musical intonation (5)
14 Bunk in a ship, train, etc (5)
16 Christen (4)
17 Essence (4)
18 Malevolent (4)
19 World's largest continent (4)

214

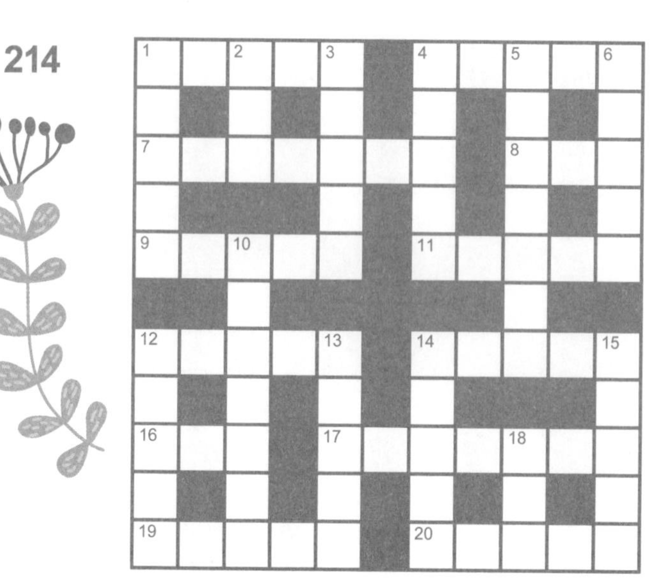

Across

1 Public transport vehicles (5)
4 Buenos ___, capital of Argentina (5)
7 No-one in particular (7)
8 Item of equipment used in baseball (3)
9 Golden yellow colour (5)
11 Markedly masculine in appearance or manner (5)
12 Accomplishment (5)
14 Fury (5)
16 ___ *Maria*, prayer to the Virgin Mary (3)
17 Body of water between Israel and Jordan (4,3)
19 Senior member of a group (5)
20 Dukedom (5)

Down

1 Area of sand sloping down to the water (5)
2 Undercover agent (3)
3 Marked by conspicuous display (5)
4 Bottomless gulf or pit (poetic) (5)
5 Daphne du Maurier novel (7)
6 Fight (3-2)
10 Lack of sophistication or worldliness (7)
12 Burn with steam (5)
13 Burdened (5)
14 Area of open or forested country (5)
15 Extremely exciting (5)
18 Hollow, flexible structure resembling a bag (3)

215

Across

1 Coffee-chocolate drink (5)
4 Sightless (5)
8 Ancient Briton (4)
9 Entry (6)
10 Call for help (inits) (3)
11 Travel on the back of an animal (4)
13 Bazaar (4)
14 Person who takes long walks in the country (7)
15 Short theatrical episode (4)
16 Matures (4)
17 Perform (3)
18 Last thing mentioned (6)
19 Polynesian rain dance (4)
21 Bushy plant (5)
22 Colour of the rainbow (5)

Down

2 Single (3)
3 Position of difficult responsibility (slang) (3,4)
5 Large mass of frozen water (7)
6 Indigestion (9)
7 Instrument panel of a vehicle (9)
8 Pupa (9)
12 Wanderer who has no established residence (7)
13 Plume (7)
20 Side sheltered from the wind (3)

216

Across

1 Legendary creature resembling a tiny old man (5)
4 Savoury taste experience (4)
6 Measure of land (4)
8 Greek storyteller (5)
9 Curved shape (8)
12 Pretentious (4)
13 Sycophant (5)
15 Unemotional person (5)
17 Drop from a height (4)
19 Offhand, curt or supercilious (8)
21 Defeats in battle (5)
22 Sediment in wine (4)
23 Compassion (4)
24 Discharge, throw out (5)

Down

1 Flat, thin circle (4)
2 British snake (5)
3 Imagine (5)
4 Practising abstention from alcohol (8)
5 Romany (5)
7 Harangue (4)
10 Vessel made of planks (4)
11 In a stringent manner (8)
14 North-country valley (4)
15 Beat with a piece of leather (5)
16 Example, instance (4)
17 Fictitious, untrue (5)
18 Province of eastern Belgium (5)
20 Absorbed, engrossed (4)

217

Across

3 Atrocious (7)

6 Semi-transparent gemstones (5)

7 Lewis ___, pen name of Charles Dodgson (7)

8 Prelude, briefly (5)

9 Small mountain lake (4)

11 Cover (4)

14 Strong sweeping cut made with a sharp instrument (4)

17 Is indebted to (4)

19 Block of gold (5)

20 Citadel (7)

21 Bear a young cow (5)

22 Point at which to retire for the night (7)

Down

1 Astrological region of constellations (6)

2 Commonly repeated word or phrase (6)

3 Berkshire town, famous for its racecourse (5)

4 Season of the year (6)

5 Permits (6)

10 Expert (3)

12 Set of eight notes (6)

13 Small active songbird (6)

15 Mrs Merkel, Chancellor of Germany (6)

16 Repugnance (6)

18 From that time (5)

218

Across

1 Cadaverous (5)
3 Carnivorous mammal of the weasel family (5)
7 Free of charge (6)
9 Standard (4)
10 Product of a hen (3)
12 Loaned (4)
13 Delicious (5)
15 Type of cobra (3)
17 Periodically repeated sequence (5)
19 Ale (4)
21 Goon (3)
22 Lowest range of tides (4)
23 Period of instruction (6)
25 Arabian country (5)
26 Cut up (5)

Down

1 Chuckle (6)
2 Pistachio or cashew, for example (3)
4 Hinged lifting tool (5)
5 Large and scholarly book (4)
6 Winged creature that transmits sleeping sickness (6,3)
8 Bother (5)
11 Breach (3)
14 Woodland plants (5)
15 Wing of an insect (3)
16 Locks of hair hanging across the forehead (6)
18 Grove of trees (5)
20 Grudging feeling (4)
24 Small ocean (3)

219

1		2		3	■	4		5	6	7
	■		■		■		■	8		
	■		■	9						
10					■		■	■		■
	■		■	11	12			13		■
14	15		■	■		■	■	16		17
■	18			19		20	■		■	
■		■	■		■	21				
22		23					■		■	
24			■		■		■		■	
25					■	26				

Across

1 Biblical tower intended to reach to heaven (5)
4 Autocratic (5)
8 One of the digits of the foot (3)
9 Continue (5,2)
10 Length of sawn timber (5)
11 Animal-drawn sledge (6)
14 Animal kept as a domestic pet (3)
16 Scarlet (3)
18 Tattered (6)
21 Allow to enter (5)
22 Depending on free oxygen or air (7)
24 Large brownish-green New Zealand parrot (3)
25 Make a request (5)
26 Link up, connect (3,2)

Down

1 Filmed life story (6)
2 Width (7)
3 Is deficient in (5)
4 Canal boat (5)
5 Enclosure for swine (3)
6 Reduce pain or discomfort (6)
7 Japanese monetary unit (3)
12 Science workshop (abbr) (3)
13 Murmur discontentedly (7)
15 Not awake (6)
17 Delay (6)
19 Informal term for a British policeman (5)
20 Type of sailboat (5)
22 Alias (inits) (3)
23 Sharp tap (3)

220

Across

1 Port ___, city at the northern end of the Gulf of Suez (4)
4 Expression used at the end of a prayer (4)
6 Cook in an oven (5)
7 Drama (4)
9 Egg-shaped, elliptical (4)
10 Hair on a horse's neck (4)
11 Peruse text (4)
12 Divide by two (5)
15 Denim trousers (5)
17 Rabbit's tail (4)
19 Marine fish (4)
20 Back part of a shoe (4)
21 Too, as well (4)
22 Slip-up (5)
23 Confront with resistance (4)
24 Fencing sword (4)

Down

1 Outstandingly good (6)
2 Wood nymph (5)
3 Detailed record of the background of a person under study (4,7)
4 Coral reef (5)
5 Africa's longest river (4)
8 Astonish (5)
13 Sung part of a piece of music (5)
14 In one's place of residence (2,4)
16 Lane down which a bowling ball is rolled (5)
17 Catch in a wire loop (5)
18 Garden toolhouse (4)

221

1			2		■	3		4		5
	■	■		■	■		■		■	
6		7		8	■	9				
	■	10			11		■		■	
12						■	13			
■	■		■	■		■	■		■	■
14				■	15	16	17			18
	■		■	19					■	
20					■	21				
	■		■		■	■		■	■	
22					■	23				

Across

1 Type of parrot (5)
3 Skin covering the top of the head (5)
6 Writing material (5)
9 Product of seabirds, used as a fertiliser (5)
10 Liquorice-flavoured seeds (5)
12 Infuriate (6)
13 Release after a security has been paid (4)
14 Black bird with a raucous call (4)
15 Living agent that carries and transmits a disease (6)
19 Beautiful young woman (5)
20 Adult insect (5)
21 Back gardens (5)
22 Prospect (5)
23 On the move (5)

Down

1 Tree, emblem of Canada (5)
2 Battleground (5)
3 Aromatic grey-green herb (4)
4 Onyx marble (9)
5 Move about in a predatory way (5)
7 Rectory (9)
8 Formation of masts, sails, etc on a vessel (3)
11 Dish out (5)
14 Strips of potato fried in deep fat (5)
16 Cambridgeshire cathedral city (3)
17 Santa ___, Father Christmas (5)
18 Vertical part of a stair (5)
19 Trunk of a tree (4)

222

1			2	■	3				4	
	■	■	5			■	■	■		■
6				■	7		8			
	■	■		■	■	■		■		■
9		10			11			12		13
	■		■	■		■	■		■	
14	15		16				17			
■		■		■	■	■		■	■	
18					19	■	20			
■		■	■	■	21			■	■	
22						■	23			

Across

1 Live in a tent (4)
3 Former name of Mumbai (6)
5 Falsehood (3)
6 Napoleon's exile island (4)
7 Rumour-monger (6)
9 Punctuation mark, bracket (11)
14 Canonised person regarded as the protector of a particular group, nation, etc (6,5)
18 Score of one stroke under par in golf (6)
20 Curse (4)
21 Branch of the British armed forces (inits) (3)
22 Metallic element, symbol Cu (6)
23 Swiss patriot, William ___ (4)

Down

1 Advance stealthily or unnoticed (5,2)
2 Flat surface on which a straight line joining any two points on it would wholly lie (5)
3 Implore (3)
4 Excuse (5)
8 Girl's name (3)
10 Decompose (3)
11 Number (3)
12 Glide over snow (3)
13 Schoolbag (7)
15 Mexican friend (5)
16 Fishing implement (3)
17 In the air (5)
19 Sin (3)

223

1		2		3	■	4		5		6
	■		■		■		■		■	
7							■	8		
	■	■	■		■		■		■	
9		10			■	11				
■	■		■	■	■	■	■		■	■
12				13	■	14				15
	■		■		■		■	■	■	
16			■	17				18		
	■		■		■		■		■	
19					■	20				

Across

1 Criminal who takes property (5)
4 Globe, planet (5)
7 Stylish and graceful (7)
8 Animal kept for companionship (3)
9 Ancient Mexican civilisation (5)
11 Hirsute (5)
12 Vegetable used as a substitute for spinach (5)
14 London skyscraper, the ___ (5)
16 Fire's remains (3)
17 Large, ocean-dwelling mammal (3,4)
19 Covered with thin horny plates (5)
20 Unit of weight equivalent to 1000 kilograms (5)

Down

1 Eighth letter of the Greek alphabet (5)
2 Anger (3)
3 Former French unit of currency (5)
4 Small portable timepiece (5)
5 Copy (7)
6 Short simple song (5)
10 Windpipe (7)
12 Form, category (5)
13 Lit by twilight (5)
14 Less than the correct amount (5)
15 Italian poet famous for writing the *Divine Comedy* (5)
18 Small hotel (3)

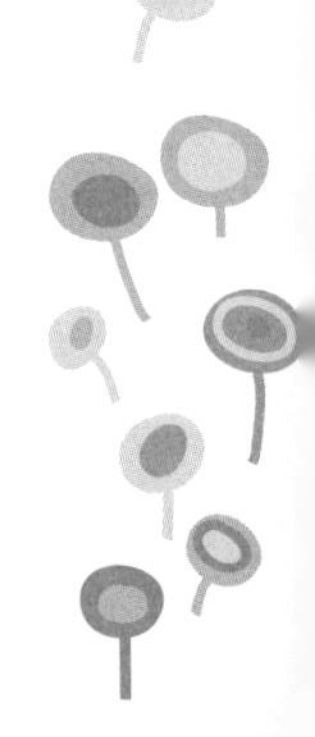

224

Across

1 Bulbous spring-flowering plant (9)
8 Mark (~) placed over the letter 'n' in Spanish (5)
9 End of a roof (5)
10 Subdivision (3)
11 Coach (5)
13 Plant used in the making of tequila (5)
15 Rod that forms the body of an arrow (5)
18 Move effortlessly (5)
20 Travel on the piste (3)
21 Small terrestrial lizard (5)
22 Give a shine to (5)
23 Hold back (9)

Down

2 Mete out (5)
3 Cloudless (5)
4 18th letter of the Greek alphabet (5)
5 Region of complete shadow (5)
6 Respected leader in national or international affairs (9)
7 Acceptance of the inevitability of failure (9)
12 No longer attached (3)
14 Sticky stuff (3)
16 Famous Mexican-American battle (5)
17 Russian rulers (5)
18 Tobacco product (5)
19 Garlic mayonnaise (5)

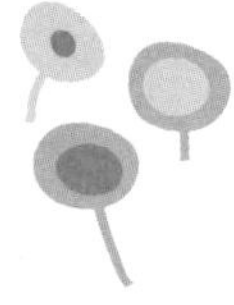

Solutions

1

A		P	A	P	E	R	C	L	I	P
N		L		A		O		O		
T	O	A	D	S		B	A	T	C	H
I		N		T	W	O		T		A
Q	U	E	U	E		T	H	O	R	N
U			Z				U			G
A	M	B	I	T		S	E	I	Z	E
R		L		O	N	O		N		R
Y	E	A	R	N		G	E	A	R	S
		D		E		G		N		O
F	R	E	E	S	T	Y	L	E		N

2

I		C		C	O	M	P	A	S	S
M	O	L	A	R			E		H	
A		U		E	N	T	R	E	A	T
G	A	M	M	A			M		L	
E		S	A	M	P	L	E		O	
S	T	Y	X		I		A	R	M	S
	H		I	N	N	A	T	E		C
	I		M			D	E	C	A	Y
C	E	D	I	L	L	A		O		T
	V		S			P	A	R	C	H
L	E	V	E	R	E	T		D		E

3

P	I	T	T		G	A	Z	E	B	O
I			R	I	O		E		E	
L	I	M	O		D	E	B	A	S	E
L			L				R		I	
A	M	A	L	G	A	M	A	T	E	
R	A	P			C			A	G	E
	F	E	L	T	T	I	P	P	E	N
	I		A				L			I
H	O	T	P	O	T		A	G	O	G
	S		A		A	N	Y			M
Z	I	G	Z	A	G		S	O	F	A

4

L	I	T	U	P		F	E	T	E	S
Y		O		R	U	L	E	R		L
M	E	T	R	O		U	R	I	N	E
P				S		I		D		E
H	I	D	E	A	N	D	S	E	E	K
		I		N		O		N		
M	A	L	A	D	J	U	S	T	E	D
A		E		C		N				R
J	U	M	B	O		C	A	I	R	O
O		M	A	N	G	E		C		N
R	O	A	R	S		S	W	E	D	E

5

	S	T	O	N	E	D	E	A	F	
C		O		O		A		D		W
O	U	T	D	O		C	H	I	N	A
M		E		N	T	H		E		T
P	I	S	T	E		A	Z	U	R	E
E			A				O			R
T	R	E	N	D		D	O	R	I	S
E		R		R	O	W		E		H
N	E	R	V	E		E	N	S	U	E
T		O		S		L		I		D
	W	R	E	S	T	L	I	N	G	

6

F	E	R	N	S		D	A	F	F	Y
A		E		T			M		A	
R		D		E	X	P	E	C	T	S
M	I	T	R	E			N		T	
E		A		D	E	A	D	S	E	A
R	A	P	T		K		S	E	N	T
S	N	E	A	K	E	R		M		H
	G		U			U	N	I	T	E
G	O	G	G	L	E	S		N		I
	R		H			T		A		S
P	A	R	T	Y		S	T	R	U	T

7

S	E	N	S	E		C	A	G	E	S
I		O		V		Y		U		P
D	I	S	T	I	N	C	T	I	V	E
E		E		L		L		D		N
S	A	Y	S		D	E	S	E	R	T
	R		H		I		E		A	
S	T	R	E	A	M		A	C	T	S
W		E		B		P		H		I
E	V	A	P	O	R	A	T	I	N	G
E		D		V		L		L		N
T	A	S	T	E		M	I	L	L	S

8

A	M	I	S	S		H		S	O	W
N		L		I	D	A	H	O		A
G	U	L	A	G		V		U		R
L		M		H		O	R	G	A	N
E	L	A	S	T	I	C		H		
R		N			R			T		O
		N		F	A	T	C	A	T	S
S	M	E	L	L		A		F		I
O		R		E		S	I	T	A	R
L		E	R	E	C	T		E		I
O	L	D		T		Y	A	R	D	S

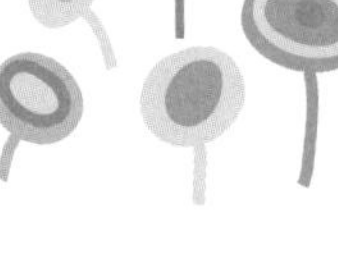

Solutions

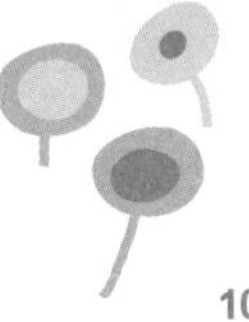

9

D	E	L	A	Y			J	E	S	T
O		A		A	R	I	A			I
G		M	I	L	E		U	S	E	D
S	T	A	T	E	M	E	N	T		A
	O		I		I		D	U	A	L
	F	I	N	A	N	C	I	N	G	
F	U	M	E		I		C		U	
I		P	R	O	S	P	E	R	E	D
V	I	S	A		C	O	D	A		I
E			N	O	E	L		I		E
S	E	T	T			L	I	N	K	S

10

P	E	R	T	H		S	C	R	A	P
A			O			T		E		A
S	T	E	W		G	U	S	S	E	T
T		L		D		F		I		I
A	S	I	D	E		F	O	L	I	O
		M	A	R	T	I	N	I		
G	R	I	M	E		N	E	E	D	S
A		N		L		G		N		H
B	R	A	Z	I	L		S	T	A	R
L		T		C			I			U
E	V	E	N	T		B	R	I	N	G

11

C	R	U	M	B		S	P	A	I	N
H			A			A		R		O
I	N	D	I	A		G	E	C	K	O
P			N		R		T			S
S	L	O	T	M	A	C	H	I	N	E
	E		A		V		N		U	
C	A	N	I	N	E	T	O	O	T	H
A			N		L		L			E
B	L	U	S	H		M	O	W	E	R
L		S		O			G			O
E	L	E	C	T		P	Y	L	O	N

12

S	K	I	R	T		C	H	A	L	K
I			U		T		E			E
G	R	A	T	E	R		R	I	C	E
N		R			E	B	B			L
A	X	E	D		E	A	S	E	D	
L		N		S	H	Y		R		T
	R	A	T	I	O		G	U	R	U
P			E	M	U			P		R
A	M	E	N		S	E	T	T	E	E
L			T		E		O			E
M	O	C	H	A		S	P	O	O	N

13

T	H	A	N	K	S		E		C	
U		B			O	P	T	I	O	N
V	A	R	Y		R		N		R	
A		U		S	E	N	A	T	O	R
L	A	P		T		O			N	
U	L	T	R	A	V	I	O	L	E	T
	C			R		S		O	R	E
L	O	O	S	E	L	Y		C		N
	H		P		O		L	A	W	N
M	O	L	A	R	S			T		I
	L		T		S	T	R	E	S	S

14

F	I	S	C	A	L			M		T
A			H		E	A	S	I	E	R
M	A	C	E		I			L		E
I			E		A	B	B	E	S	S
L	E	A	S	H		A		A		P
I		B	E	A	N	B	A	G		A
A		S		K		E	V	E	N	S
R	I	C	H	E	S		A			S
I		O			E		T	A	X	I
S	U	N	S	E	T		A			N
E		D			S	T	R	O	N	G

15

F		C		K		M	A	T	C	H
R	E	A	L	I	T	Y		O		A
A		T		L		T		R		B
M	O	T	E	L		H	A	N	O	I
E		L	I	E			W			T
	S	E	G	R	E	G	A	T	E	
T			H			E	K	E		K
E	A	R	T	H		Y	E	A	R	N
X		A		O		S		S		I
A		C		P	R	E	V	E	N	T
S	C	E	N	E		R		T		S

16

S	H	A	C	K		A	N	N	O	Y
T		L		E			E		M	
R	U	B	E	N	S		R	E	A	D
A		U			H	A	V	E	N	
T	A	M	P	E	R		O	L	I	O
U			R		I		U			I
M	A	R	E		V	E	S	S	E	L
	G	A	B	L	E			A		W
L	A	N	E		L	I	T	T	L	E
	T		N			M		I		L
L	E	N	D	S		P	A	N	E	L

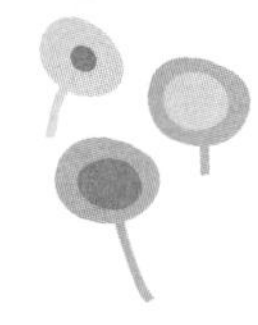

Solutions

17

C	L	E	R	K		F	A	L	S	E
A			O		P		L			C
N	E	A	T	E	R		I	N	C	H
O		B			I		B			O
P	L	A	Y	A	C	T	I	N	G	
Y		T		F	E	E		U		S
	K	E	T	T	L	E	D	R	U	M
A			A		E			S		U
D	I	G	S		S	H	I	E	L	D
E			T		S		R			G
N	A	K	E	D		S	K	A	T	E

18

C	H	O	P	S		F	O	C	U	S
O		W		H		A		O		P
A	T	E	L	I	E	R		P	E	A
T				N		C		I		C
S	T	R	A	Y		E	V	O	K	E
O		E						U		H
F	I	F	T	H		I	S	S	U	E
A		L		I		S				A
R	Y	E		V	I	A	D	U	C	T
M		C		E		A		S		E
S	I	T	E	S		C	H	A	I	R

19

R	H	O	D	E	I	S	L	A	N	D
	E		E		R			V		W
M	A	S	S		R	E	V	E	R	E
	T		T	O	E			N		L
C	H	O	R	A	L		M	U	L	L
H		F	O	R	E	S	E	E		E
I	F	F	Y		V	E	R	S	E	D
S		B			A	T	M		L	
E	V	E	L	Y	N		A	S	B	O
L		A			C		I		O	
S	E	T	T	L	E	D	D	O	W	N

20

C	L	A	I	M		A	O	R	T	A
O		C		A			U		I	
N		C		G	L	I	T	T	E	R
S	O	R	T	I	E		B		R	
I		U		C	A	B	I	N	E	T
G	L	E	N		K		D	A	D	O
N	O	S	E	B	A	G		M		N
	N		E		G	N	E	I	S	S
D	E	A	D	S	E	A		B		U
	L		L			R		I		R
R	Y	D	E	R		L	E	A	S	E

21

T	O	G	A		W	A	Y	L	A	Y
I			B	E	E				P	
S	E	M	I		T	O	P	H	A	T
S			D				E		C	
U	N	D	E	R	S	T	A	T	E	
E		U			I			O		N
	F	O	R	E	C	A	S	T	L	E
	L		I				C			E
B	A	O	B	A	B		A	M	I	D
	M				A	W	L			L
B	E	H	E	A	D		D	O	L	E

22

M	O	T	E	T		S	C	A	N	T
U		I		R		A		S		I
C	A	T	C	A	L	L		S	A	T
U				I		A		U		H
S	A	L	O	N		D	R	A	K	E
		E						G		
C	E	A	S	E		C	H	E	E	R
O		R		X		I				E
S	O	N		I	N	G	R	A	T	E
T		E		L		A		F		D
S	P	R	E	E		R	E	T	R	Y

23

B	U	C	K	E	T		S		C	
A		E			H	O	Y	D	E	N
R	A	R	E		O		R		N	
G		E		A	R	T	I	S	T	S
R	E	B	E	L		R	A	I	S	E
A		R		L	A	Y		G		C
P	H	A	S	E		O	W	N	E	R
H	A	L	C	Y	O	N		P		E
	T		U		P		C	O	S	T
A	C	C	R	U	E			S		L
	H		F		N	E	A	T	L	Y

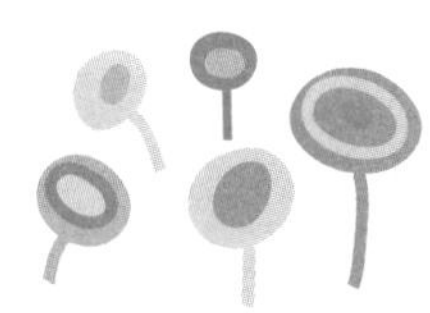

24

T	A	X	I			R	H	I	N	E
H			N	I	L	E		N		N
R	U	G	S			M		T		E
E		H	I	S	T	O	G	R	A	M
W	R	O	T	E		T		O		Y
		S	U	C	C	E	E	D		
B		T		R		S	L	U	S	H
A	U	T	H	E	N	T	I	C		Y
C		O		T			C	E	D	E
O		W		L	E	V	I			N
N	A	N	N	Y			T	U	B	A

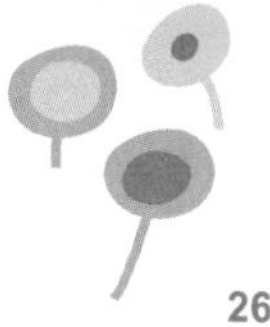

Solutions

25

J	E	W	E	L		I	N	P	U	T
	R		C		M			R		A
T	A	P	S		E	X	C	E	S	S
E			T	I	C			S		T
S	O	F	A		H		D	I	M	E
T		A	S	H	A	M	E	D		L
P	O	N	Y		N		S	E	R	E
I		C			I	N	K			S
L	A	I	R	D	S		T	O	G	S
O		E			M		O		E	
T	A	R	D	Y		A	P	P	L	E

26

M	U	S	T	Y		F	I	S	H	Y
I		C		A			N			A
M	O	H	A	W	K		S	A	S	H
I		M		S	I	L	T			O
C	H	I	C		N		A	L	S	O
		D	E	M	E	S	N	E		
Y	E	T	I		T		T	A	F	T
O			L	A	I	D		F		O
D	E	L	I		C	U	R	L	E	W
E			N			M		E		E
L	O	U	G	H		B	E	T	E	L

27

S	M	A	L	L			L	A	S	S
U		N		I	N	T	O			A
M		N		M		U	N	C	U	T
P	L	U	M	B	I	N	G			A
	O	L	I	O		E	S	S	E	N
	L		S				H		V	
S	L	O	T	H		P	O	L	E	
T			R	O	A	S	T	I	N	G
A	I	D	E	S		A		V		L
R			S	E	A	L		E		E
T	A	P	S			M	A	N	G	E

28

B	I	G	B	E	N			D		T
A			I		U	N	W	I	S	E
S	L	A	L	O	M			S		P
I			L		B	A	T	T	L	E
C	H	A	O	S		L		A		E
		S	W	A	G	M	A	N		
B		U		L		S	E	T	U	P
I	N	S	I	T	U		R			A
L		U			S	C	A	L	D	S
G	L	A	N	C	E		T			T
E		L			D	E	E	P	L	Y

29

S	E	R	U	M			S	E	A	M
H		A		A	B	H	O	R		A
E	L	F		G			R	A	M	S
D	E	T	A	I	L		D			O
	V			C	I	T	I	Z	E	N
	E		S	A	V	E	D		V	
P	E	R	P	L	E	X			E	
E			H		S	T	R	O	N	G
A	C	H	E			I		A	T	E
C		O	R	I	E	L		T		T
H	O	P	E			E	T	H	O	S

30

N	O	I	S	E		C	A	C	T	I
A			H			A		E		M
C	O	P	E	S		S	C	R	U	B
H		R	E	A	C	T		V		U
O	V	E	R	D	O		C	A	K	E
		O			P			N		
D	I	R	T		S	A	L	T	E	D
O		D		G	E	N	I	E		R
G	H	A	N	A		T	E	S	T	Y
G		I		V			G			E
O	U	N	C	E		C	E	D	A	R

31

S	E	N	T	E	N	T	I	O	U	S
T		O		S		O		W		T
A	T	O	M	S		T	E	N	S	E
G		S		A	W	E		E		A
E	M	E	R	Y		M	O	D	E	M
M			A				V			E
A	M	O	N	G		S	A	T	A	N
N		U		I	R	K		O		G
A	C	T	O	R		E	N	N	U	I
G		E		T		I		G		N
E	A	R	T	H	E	N	W	A	R	E

32

B	A	R	B	S		F	U	M	E	S
	N		A		V			A		U
A	V	O	N		I		S	L	U	G
	I		D	E	S	P	O	T		G
S	L	O	W		U		V	A	S	E
O			A	M	A	Z	E			S
L	O	N	G		L		R	O	O	T
O		I	O	D	I	N	E		R	
M	A	N	N		S		I	R	A	N
O		T			E		G		T	
N	E	H	R	U		A	N	G	E	L

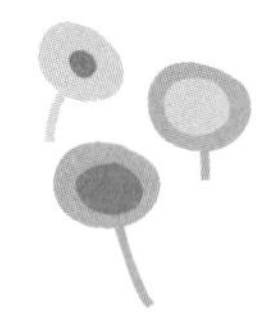

Solutions

33

C	O	B	W	E	B			M		O
O			I		L	I	Z	A	R	D
N	O	U	N		A			T		D
G			C	O	N	S	P	I	R	E
A	B	S	E	N	C	E		N		R
		C		S		V		E		
C		A		E	L	E	M	E	N	T
R	I	N	G	T	O	N	E			E
E		D			O		T	A	K	E
A	B	A	C	U	S		E			M
M		L			E	G	R	E	S	S

34

A	L	I	G	N			S	A	I	D
D			L		W	A	R	N		I
J	A	C	O	B	I		I	S	I	S
U			V	A	T			W		O
D	E	S	E	R	T		V	E	R	B
I		U		S	I	T		R		E
C	A	R	D		C	E	A	S	E	D
A		P			I	M	P			I
T	E	A	L		S	P	H	E	R	E
O		S	E	E	M		I			N
R	U	S	K			E	D	I	C	T

35

C	A	R	D	S		A		C	O	W
A				A	W	F	U	L		I
L	I	C	I	T		F		E		N
I		H		A		I	D	A	H	O
P	H	A	R	Y	N	X		R		
H		R			A			A		N
		L		A	B	S	E	N	C	E
G	R	A	S	S		T		C		A
A		T		P		E	R	E	C	T
I		A	L	I	K	E				L
T	E	N		C		R	A	L	L	Y

36

S	E	P	I	A		G	R	A	S	P
U		A		L		U		M		I
C	O	N	F	I	N	E		A	S	S
K				A		S		T		T
S	O	R	T	S		S	W	E	D	E
		E						U		
S	L	A	N	T		S	H	R	U	B
H		C		U		C				A
A	F	T		L	E	A	R	N	E	D
K		O		L		R		O		G
E	E	R	I	E		F	O	R	C	E

37

S	O	C	I	A	L		B		D	
E		R			O	D	I	O	U	S
T	H	I	N	G	S		P		V	
T		S		A	T	E	L	I	E	R
E	D	I	T	S			A		T	
E		S	A	P	I	E	N	T		E
	E		B			A	E	S	O	P
I	D	Y	L	L	I	C		E		O
	G		E		B	H	U	T	A	N
S	A	F	A	R	I			S		Y
	R		U		S	C	R	E	A	M

38

T	H	U	G			I	N	F	E	R
H			O	V	E	N		O		U
U	L	N	A			V		R		S
M		A	T	O	N	E	M	E	N	T
B	A	R	E			N		C		Y
		R	E	C	I	T	A	L		
T		A		A			S	O	O	N
H	I	T	O	R	M	I	S	S		O
I		I		E			E	E	L	S
N		V		S	E	E	S			E
G	U	E	S	S			S	L	I	D

39

	U	P	P	E	R	C	A	S	E	
A		I		R		O		A		J
L	L	A	M	A		D	E	L	T	A
P		N		S	E	E		S		C
E	L	O	P	E		D	R	A	N	K
N			E				I			F
H	Y	E	N	A		A	M	O	U	R
O		A		L	A	D		M		O
R	U	R	A	L		D	R	E	G	S
N		T		O		E		G		T
	S	H	O	W	T	R	I	A	L	

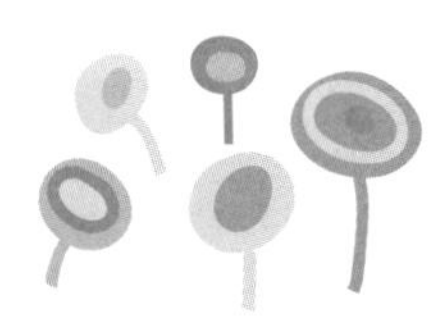

40

S	I	N	B	A	D			A		M
T			O		A	T	O	M	I	C
O	P	E	N	A	I	R		O		C
I			S		S	I	G	N		O
C	H	E	A	P		P		G	U	Y
		D	I	S	C	U	S	S		
S	R	I		Y		P	A	T	C	H
O		T	A	C	T		L			A
L		I		H	O	R	I	Z	O	N
A	Z	O	R	E	S		V			K
R		N			S	H	A	N	D	Y

Solutions

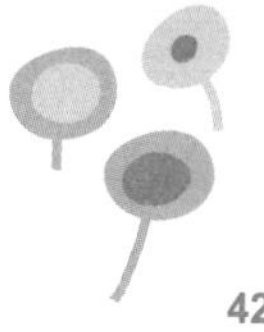

41

I	N	D	I	G	O		B		R	
N		E			R	E	A	D	E	R
T	A	P	E		A		G		S	
A		R		E	L	A	S	T	I	C
N	O	I	S	Y		I		A	N	Y
D		V		R	I	D		L		S
E	W	E		I		E	V	I	C	T
M	A	D	N	E	S	S		S		I
	G		A		O		E	M	I	T
D	O	M	I	N	O			A		I
	N		L		T	E	N	N	I	S

42

B	A	N	T	A	M			M		C
A			U		A	R	M	A	D	A
L	A	T	R	I	N	E		D		P
E			B		I	N	C	O	M	E
S	I	R	O	C	C	O		N		R
		E	T	A		W	I	N		
T		S		P	A	N	C	A	K	E
W	A	P	I	T	I		E			V
I		I		O	R	G	A	N	Z	A
R	E	T	I	R	E		G			N
L		E			R	H	E	S	U	S

43

T	O	A	S	T		S	P	O	C	K
I		D		H			O		O	
D	E	A	C	O	N		L	I	M	P
I		P	O	S	I	T	I	V	E	
N	U	T	M	E	G		C	Y	S	T
G			P		G		E			E
S	A	V	E		A	L	M	O	N	D
	M	A	T	E	R	I	A	L		I
D	A	T	E		D	E	N	I	R	O
	Z		N			I		V		U
T	E	E	T	H		N	E	E	D	S

44

K	N	A	C	K		A	C	T	O	R
I		D		N	A	P		R		I
R	O	D	E	O		I	C	I	N	G
O		L		T	I	N		B		I
V	I	E	W	S		G	R	E	E	D
	N		A				Y		G	
A	N	G	S	T		S	E	D	G	E
W		U		I	O	U		R		L
A	D	M	I	T		S	N	A	R	E
I		B		A	S	H		W		C
T	H	O	R	N		I	N	L	E	T

45

C	H	A	P	S		E	K	I	N	G
O		J		O			E		U	
N		A		M	A	N	D	A	T	E
F	A	R	C	E			G		R	
E			L	O	U	S	E		I	
R	A	Y	O	N		U	R	B	A	N
	L		S	E	I	N	E			I
	C		E			R	E	S	I	N
R	O	S	S	I	N	I		O		E
	V		E			S		F		T
B	E	R	T	H		E	N	T	R	Y

46

S	T	A	R	C	H			S		R
A			I		A	C	T	I	V	E
T	U	N	N	E	L			D		A
Y			S		F	R	I	E	N	D
R	O	M	E	O		I		C		Y
		U		V	E	T		A		
M		M		E		E	R	R	O	R
E	M	B	A	R	K		U			A
R		L			N	E	L	S	O	N
G	H	E	T	T	O		E			C
E		D			W	A	R	M	T	H

47

S	C	A	L	E	S		M		H	
C		S			C	R	A	Y	O	N
R	E	T	I	N	A		T		L	
I		U		E	N	G	R	O	S	S
B	I	T		S			O		T	
E	L	E	C	T	I	O	N	E	E	R
	L		I			V		B	R	A
R	E	S	P	I	T	E		B		R
	G		H		O	N	L	I	N	E
P	A	P	E	R	S			N		L
	L		R		S	H	A	G	G	Y

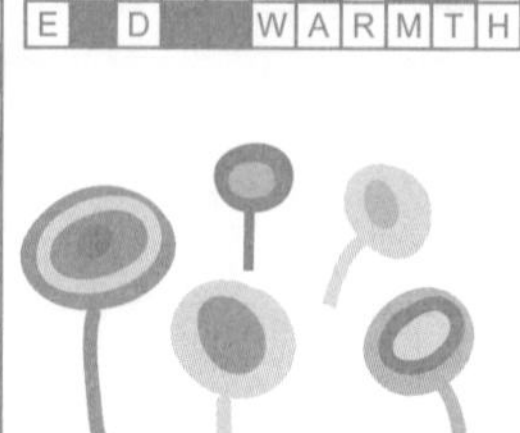

48

P	I	P	E	S		C	U	P	I	D
L		O		I		R		I		R
A	N	T	E	N	N	A		L	E	O
N				K		S		S		V
T	I	C	K	S		S	I	N	C	E
		A						E		
P	A	L	E	S		S	C	R	A	M
U		Y		O		H				O
F	O	P		N	E	R	V	O	U	S
F		S		I		U		W		E
S	T	O	I	C		B	A	N	N	S

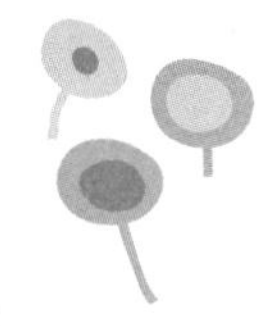

Solutions

49

C	O	M	I	C		P	I	T	T	A
A		O		O	U	R		I		R
B		O		N		E		T	A	R
A	B	R	A	C	A	D	A	B	R	A
L				E		O		I	T	S
	T	R	A	N	S	M	I	T	S	
G	E	E		T		I				F
R	E	V	E	R	E	N	T	I	A	L
O	N	O		A		A		D		O
S		K		T	O	T		L		U
S	I	E	G	E		E	R	E	C	T

50

	T	A	S	T	E	L	E	S	S	
P		B		O		O		C		I
A	G	A	I	N		D	R	A	W	N
P		S		G	I	G		B		T
E	T	H	O	S		E	N	S	U	E
R			W				E			S
B	I	L	L	S		A	B	B	O	T
A		A		A	W	L		A		I
C	O	R	G	I		T	R	Y	O	N
K		V		N		A		O		E
	R	A	P	T	U	R	O	U	S	

51

G	L	O	R	I	A			R		L
U			A		B	R	U	I	S	E
I	C	E	F	L	O	E		V		P
L			T		R	A	V	I	N	E
D	E	S	E	R	T	S		E		R
		I	R	A		O	A	R		
F		N		C	A	N	V	A	S	S
E	S	C	H	E	W		A			E
A		E		M	A	R	T	I	N	I
S	H	R	I	E	K		A			N
T		E			E	N	R	A	G	E

52

P	Y	R	A	M	I	D		O		B
O		E		A		I	N	N	E	R
P	A	T	E	N		V		U		O
U		O		T	R	A	N	S	I	T
P	U	R	E	R			O			H
		T	R	A	M	M	E	L		
S			I			A	L	A	R	M
A	V	E	N	G	E	R		R		U
U		A		E		I	D	I	O	T
C	A	S	T	E		N		A		E
Y		T		S	C	E	N	T	E	D

53

C	O	P	R	A		K	N	E	A	D
R		L		M			A		M	
O		A		O	V	E	R	E	A	T
W	O	T	A	N			C		Z	
D		E	G	G	W	H	I	T	E	
S	T	A	G		A		S	O	D	A
	S	U	R	P	R	I	S	E		V
	H		I			N	I	C	H	E
M	I	N	E	R	A	L		A		R
	R		V			A		P		S
U	T	T	E	R		W	A	S	T	E

54

S		O		B		S	I	B	Y	L
T	O	R	P	E	D	O		O		I
A		N		T		R		R		N
S	H	A	F	T		T	H	E	M	E
H		T	I	E			A			N
	T	E	R	R	O	R	I	S	T	
B			S			U	R	N		A
E	A	R	T	H		D	Y	I	N	G
A		A		A		D		P		A
M		C		C	L	E	M	E	N	T
S	T	E	A	K		R		R		E

55

F	L	E	E	T		W	I	R	E	S
	E		M		M			I		E
K	I	W	I		O	R	I	S	O	N
I			G	N	U			S		T
D	O	O	R		S		M	O	O	R
G		R	E	N	E	W	A	L		Y
L	O	P	E		T		H	E	R	B
O		H			R	A	J			O
V	I	E	N	N	A		O	N	Y	X
E		U			P		N		E	
S	U	S	H	I		A	G	A	T	E

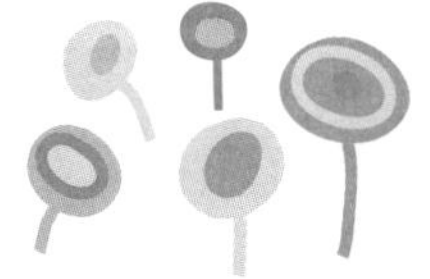

56

M	E	R	C	E	R			B		S
O		I		C		B	L	O	O	M
S		O		O	I	L		S		O
S	A	T	I	N		I	N	N		O
	X			O		N		I		T
B	E	T		M	A	D		A	S	H
R		E		I		A			E	
I		A	R	C		L	A	T	C	H
D		P		A	L	L		O		A
G	H	O	U	L		E		U		N
E		T			H	Y	B	R	I	D

Solutions

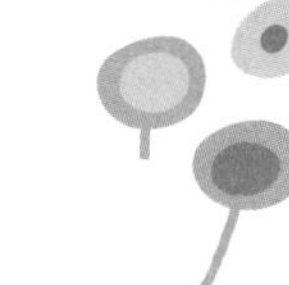

57

A	L	O	O	F		E		D	I	M
M				R	A	D	I	I		O
O	B	E	S	E		G		G		S
E		N		E		E	D	I	T	S
B	E	S	I	D	E	S		T		
A		N			R			A		U
		A		K	R	E	M	L	I	N
S	T	R	A	Y		P		I		S
L		I		L		E	N	S	U	E
I		N	A	I	V	E				E
P	U	G		E		S	P	A	I	N

58

S		A		D	I	C	T	A	T	E
C	O	N	G	A			A		E	
A		N		L	A	P	L	A	N	D
R	O	U	T	E			E		N	
A		L	E	S	S	E	N		I	
B	A	S	S		U		T	O	S	S
	G		T	A	M	P	E	R		T
	H		A			A	D	D	E	R
T	A	C	T	I	C	S		E		I
	S		O			T	H	A	N	K
S	T	E	R	I	L	E		L		E

59

B	E	N	U	M	B			I		C
A			T		O	C	U	L	A	R
S	H	R	O	U	D			L		U
E		A	P	P	E	N	D	A	G	E
R	E	M	I	T		A		T		T
		P	A	U	L	I	N	E		
B		A		R		L	O	A	T	H
E	N	G	I	N	E	E	R	S		O
L		I			O	D	D	E	S	T
L	I	N	D	E	N		I			L
E		G			S	I	C	I	L	Y

60

S	A	L	O	N		C	R	O	S	S
C			C			H		P		P
R	I	S	E		G	R	A	P	P	A
U		T	A	T		I		O		C
B	L	I	N	I		S	E	R	G	E
		P		R	A	T		T		
A	B	U	S	E		E	L	U	D	E
R		L		L		N	A	N		M
E	N	A	M	E	L		S	E	E	M
T		T		S			S			E
E	V	E	N	S		B	O	A	S	T

61

B	U	S	H	E	L		L		N	
O		E			Y	E	O	M	A	N
B	O	W	S	E	R		O		S	
C		A		P	E	R	S	I	S	T
A		G		I			E		A	
T	R	E	A	C	H	E	R	O	U	S
	E		B			V		R		E
N	A	I	R	O	B	I		A		C
	S		O		E	L	I	C	I	T
S	O	N	A	T	A			L		O
	N		D		M	E	T	E	O	R

62

C	O	O	L		S	A	D	D	L	E
H		A	D	O					Y	
A	H	O	Y		S	T	U	P	I	D
L		E					R		N	
E	V	E	R	Y	T	H	I	N	G	
T		F			I			A		H
	S	T	E	R	E	O	T	Y	P	E
	C		E				A			A
G	A	L	L	O	P		S	O	U	R
	R				A	V	E			T
B	E	A	U	T	Y		R	A	G	S

63

S	C	O	W	L		A	B	Y	S	S
C			O		P		E			E
R	O	C	O	C	O		R	O	A	N
I		H			S		Y			T
P	A	I	N		T	O	L	L	S	
T		N			H			E		C
	S	A	M	O	A		N	E	I	L
T			I		S			C		O
A	G	E	D		T	Y	P	H	U	S
L			G		E		E			E
C	A	B	E	R		A	W	A	R	D

64

C	A	P	E	R		C	A	D	R	E
A		I		O			S		H	
R	E	L	A	Y	S		E	P	I	C
N		O		A	T	O	P		N	
A	T	T	I	L	A		T	H	O	U
G			N		T			I		N
E	L	A	N		U	N	C	O	R	K
	E		A	U	R	A		P		E
F	A	I	R		E	S	T	E	E	M
	S		D			A		R		P
C	H	E	S	S		L	E	A	N	T

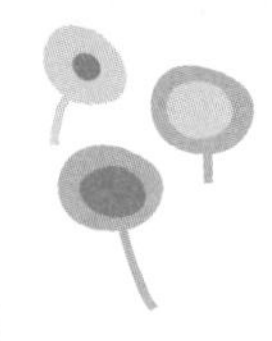

Solutions

65

S	U	M	P		T	I	G	H	T	S
H			A	C	I	D			R	
A	V	O	N		C	A	N	C	E	R
B			I			H			N	
B	L	A	C	K	B	O	A	R	D	
Y		G			A			U		R
	C	O	N	T	R	A	V	E	N	E
	R			A			O			M
V	A	N	I	S	H		D	I	V	E
	W			T	A	C	K			D
A	L	W	A	Y	S		A	L	L	Y

66

S	E	P	I	A		C	O	B	R	A
E		E		M		U		R		R
P	A	N	N	I	E	R		A	D	O
A				S		D		V		S
L	I	S	T	S		S	A	U	T	E
		I						R		
J	A	N	E	T		S	W	A	M	P
U		U		I		O				O
M	A	O		M	E	N	A	C	E	S
B		U		E		A		A		S
O	U	S	T	S		R	A	N	G	E

67

M	E	N	D	S		A	L	I	E	N
I			E			N		N		I
N	O	B	L	E		N	U	D	G	E
U			H			O		I		C
S	A	T	I	S	F	Y		A	G	E
	W			H		E			A	
P	E	P		E	N	D	O	R	S	E
R		O		R			T			A
A	D	L	I	B		C	H	O	P	S
N		I		E			E			E
G	L	O	A	T		K	R	I	L	L

68

T	U	R	F			T	U	L	I	P
H			E	L	B	A		O		A
R	O	A	D			I		R		L
O		M	O	N	O	L	O	G	U	E
B	A	S	R	A		P		N		R
		T	A	G	L	I	N	E		
S		E		A		P	E	T	E	R
W	O	R	K	S	H	E	E	T		I
A		D		A			D	E	A	F
M		A		K	I	L	L			L
I	A	M	B	I			E	R	N	E

69

R	A	D	A	R		B		E	E	L
E			L	E	M	O	N	S		A
A	G	A	I	N		A		C		C
P		L		O	A	T	C	A	K	E
E	C	L	A	I	R			L		
D		O		R	O	W		A		D
		W			S	O	O	T	H	E
C	H	A	U	C	E	R		O		C
A		N		U		K	O	R	E	A
S		C	O	B	W	E	B			D
H	U	E		E		R	I	D	G	E

70

S	Q	U	I	B		A	D	D	L	E
E		S		R			A		E	
C		S	C	A	L	L	Y	W	A	G
T	H	R	O	W			D		D	
O			F	L	O	O	R		E	
R	E	E	F		U		E	A	R	L
	I		E	X	T	R	A			A
	G		E			E	M	P	T	Y
C	H	I	P	O	L	A	T	A		M
	T		O			D		P		A
W	Y	A	T	T		Y	E	A	R	N

71

S	A	L	V	O		S	H	A	L	L
P		E		V	I	P		L		E
I	M	A	G	O		I		T	A	T
R			R	I	L	L		A		H
E	B	B	E	D		L	A	R	G	E
	O		B				B		Y	
K	O	R	E	A		C	H	A	M	P
N		E		S	O	L	O			R
O	R	B		P		I	R	A	T	E
L		U		E	L	M		C		S
L	A	T	I	N		B	A	T	H	S

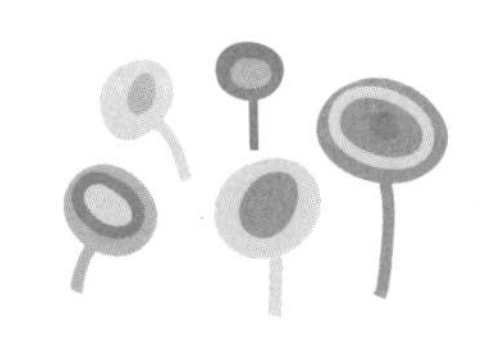

72

P	A	N	E	L		B	L	I	S	S
E			R			A		N		E
A	C	E	R			S	L	A	V	E
C		P	A	I	N	S		M		D
E	D	I	T			E	P	O	X	Y
		C	U	R	A	T	O	R		
S	P	U	M	E			T	A	R	N
I		R		C	A	R	A	T		A
G	E	E	S	E			B	A	C	K
H		A		S			L			E
T	U	N	I	S		B	E	A	R	D

Solutions

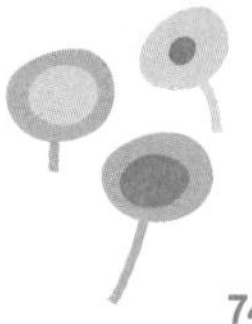

73

S		C		Y		S	C	O	W	L
T	O	R	P	E	D	O		A		A
E		U		M		U		R		B
E	L	I	D	E		P	A	S	S	E
D		S	I	N			L			L
	P	E	R	I	S	C	O	P	E	
B			G			A	H	A		B
A	S	T	E	R		B	A	L	S	A
L		A		O		I		L		G
E		L		S	U	N	R	I	S	E
D	E	L	A	Y		S		D		L

74

S	H	O	P	S		M	O	I	S	T
L			R			A		M		R
I	N	C	A		S	C	A	M	P	I
N		A	I	R		A		O		A
G	E	N	R	E		R	A	V	E	L
		D	I	P	L	O	M	A		
I	C	I	E	R		N	A	B	O	B
S		D		I		I	L	L		E
A	Z	A	L	E	A		G	E	A	R
A		T		V			A			N
C	R	E	T	E		S	M	O	K	E

75

S	L	A	C	K	S		N		C	
A		N			T	R	O	C	H	E
B	O	N	N		E		U		A	
O		O		S	P	O	N	S	O	R
T	E	T	R	A		C		U	S	E
A		A		U	G	H		P		V
G	O	T		D		R	E	E	V	E
E	R	E	M	I	T	E		R		R
	G		A		R		F	I	B	S
T	A	H	I	T	I			O		A
	N		D		P	L	U	R	A	L

76

O		V		S	T	A	U	N	C	H
P	O	A	C	H			N		A	
T		L		E	V	I	D	E	N	T
I	N	U	R	E			E		A	
C		E	A	R	N	E	R		P	
S	U	D	S		E		S	U	E	T
	N		H	I	T	L	E	R		A
	T		N			Y	A	C	H	T
F	R	E	E	M	A	N		H		T
	U		S			C	A	I	R	O
M	E	S	S	I	A	H		N		O

77

S	O	F	I	A		E	G	Y	P	T
P		E		L			E		E	
R		T	E	L	L	I	N	G	L	Y
A	Z	A	L	E	A		U		V	
W			S	N	U	F	F		I	
L	A	M	E		N		L	I	S	P
	M		W	E	D	G	E			R
	P		H		E	N	C	A	S	E
C	E	L	E	B	R	A	T	E		F
	R		R			R		R		E
L	E	V	E	R		L	A	Y	E	R

78

P	A	T	C	H		V	I	V	I	D
E			R			O		O		R
A	L	R	E	A	D	Y		T	H	E
R			A		E	A	S	E		A
L	E	T	T	I	N	G		D	A	M
	Y		E	N	T	E	R		G	
S	E	A		V	I	S	I	T	O	R
H		D	O	E	S		D			I
O	D	D		S	T	U	D	I	E	D
E		E		T			L			G
S	I	D	E	S		W	E	A	V	E

79

T	H	R	I	L	L		F		A	
Y		O			U	S	U	R	P	S
P	A	M	P	A	S		S		R	
E		A		C	H	A	S	S	I	S
C	Y	N	I	C		C	Y	C	L	E
A		T		U		R		O		A
S	W	I	S	S		O	G	R	E	S
T	I	C	K	E	T	S		P		H
	G		E		A	S	P	I	R	E
C	H	A	I	N	S			O		L
	T		N		K	E	R	N	E	L

80

P	I	O	U	S			H	O	P	S
U		V		H	U	L	A			W
F		E		O			R	A	K	E
F	I	R	S	T	A	I	D			P
	T		P		M		S	I	F	T
	E		O	L	I	V	E		I	
S	M	U	T		T		L		T	
P			L	O	Y	A	L	I	S	T
I	S	L	E			B		B		O
L			S	O	M	E		I		G
L	E	G	S			D	I	S	C	O

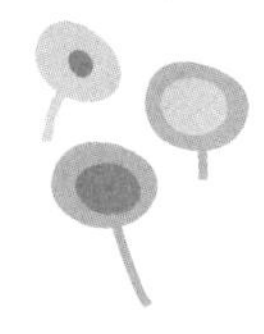

Solutions

81

C	R	U	S	H		I	S	S	U	E
	A		W		H			P		X
P	Y	R	E		E	R	R	A	N	T
A			E	T	A			N		R
L	A	S	T	E	D		S	I	D	E
A		W	I	N	S	O	M	E		M
T	R	E	E		T	W	E	L	V	E
A		A			A	L	L			L
B	A	T	H	E	R		T	R	A	Y
L		E			T		E		W	
E	A	R	T	H		D	R	U	N	K

82

S	E	A	B	E	D			D		E
I			O		O	R	D	E	R	S
S	L	A	T	E	S			C		S
A			H		S	T	R	I	K	E
L	O	S	E	S		Y		D		X
		T	R	A	M	P	L	E		
M		E		G		E	A	S	E	L
A	F	L	O	A	T		D			E
Y		L			E	N	I	G	M	A
O	R	A	T	O	R		E			V
R		R			M	O	S	Q	U	E

83

B	A	T	H	E	R		B	E	T	A
L		A		A			O			S
I		P	A	R	A	L	Y	S	I	S
N		E		W			C		G	
G	U	S	T	A	V		O	G	L	E
	D		E	X	I	S	T		O	
O	D	I	N		A	U	T	H	O	R
	E		U			T		O		O
P	R	E	O	C	C	U	P	Y		U
A			U			R		L		N
W	I	G	S		D	E	F	E	N	D

84

A	S	H	E	S		G	A	R	B	O
L		A		T			M		I	
C		M		A	L	M	A	N	A	C
A	M	B	E	R			Z		S	
Z		U		T	R	O	O	P	E	R
A	G	R	A		A		N	O	D	E
R	A	G	T	I	M	E		S		C
	R		H			A	I	S	L	E
O	N	G	O	I	N	G		E		I
	E		M			E		S		P
A	R	M	E	D		R	E	S	E	T

85

C		C	O	W	A	R	D	I	C	E
O		O		H		A		T		
S	H	A	M	E		N	A	C	R	E
T		T	A	R	N	I	S	H		A
A	L	I	C	E		S	T	Y	E	S
R			R				O			T
I	D	E	A	L		P	U	R	E	E
C		I	M	A	G	I	N	E		R
A	U	G	E	R		E	D	U	C	E
		H		V		C		S		G
T	E	T	E	A	T	E	T	E		G

86

S	A	G	O			D	O	L	L	S
O			B	A	B	E		I		O
R	I	P	E			V		B	A	D
R		E	Y	E	S	O	R	E		O
Y	O	N		N		T		R	U	M
		P	A	T	R	I	O	T		
E	A	U		R		O		I	N	S
N		S	H	A	N	N	O	N		N
D	O	H		I			P	E	S	O
O		E		L	I	E	U			U
W	I	R	E	S			S	O	F	T

87

P		S	T	A	G	E	D	O	O	R
A		E		V		V		N		
R	A	D	I	I		O	K	A	P	I
A		G		A	U	K		I		N
G	L	E	N	N		E	G	R	E	T
R			O				A			H
A	V	O	W	S		A	D	O	B	E
P		U		I	L	L		S		D
H	A	T	E	D		O	U	I	J	A
		E		L		U		E		R
B	A	R	T	E	N	D	E	R		K

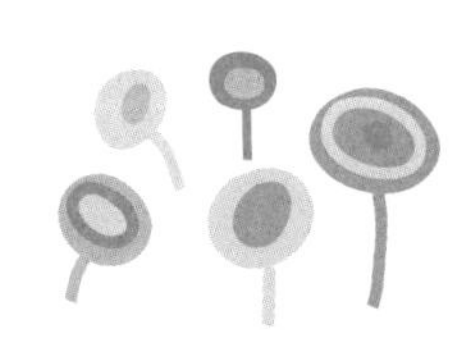

88

B	A	N	J	O		B	A	K	E	D
E		I		K			F			R
R	O	G	E	R	S		T	R	U	E
A		E		A	C	M	E			W
T	Y	R	E		H	O	R	S	E	
E		I		R	O	B		W		C
	L	A	P	E	L		S	E	L	L
S			A	D	A	M		E		E
P	U	M	P		R	O	S	T	E	R
U			E			O		E		I
R	E	A	R	S		T	U	N	I	C

Solutions

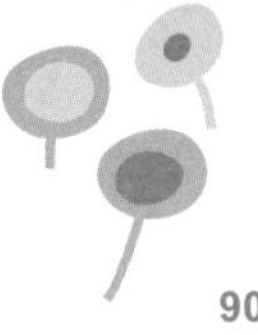

89

O		C		R	O	O	S	T	E	D
S	N	A	K	E			H		U	
M		T		T	O	R	R	E	N	T
O	S	C	A	R			I		U	
S		H		O	F	F	E	N	C	E
I	D	E	A		O		K	O	H	L
S	I	S	T	E	R	S		X		I
	W		T			W	A	I	S	T
M	A	F	I	O	S	I		O		I
	L		R			N	O	U	N	S
F	I	R	E	B	U	G		S		T

90

V	O	I	C	E		M	I	L	L	S
I			A			E		E		H
S	T	A	N	D	A	R	D	S		O
I			A			E		S		W
T	A	I	L		E	L	B	O	W	S
		M		A	N	Y		N		
F	R	I	E	N	D		A	S	I	A
A		T		N			W			G
C		A	B	U	N	D	A	N	C	E
E		T		A			R			N
S	H	E	L	L		B	E	A	S	T

91

B	A	N	A	L		S	C	R	I	M
R			R		R		U			I
U	P	S	I	D	E		F	O	A	L
I	O	T	A		I		F			K
S	T	O	N	E	M	A	S	O	N	
E		M			B			V		P
	C	A	P	P	U	C	C	I	N	O
P			R		R		A	N	E	W
U	N	T	O		S	C	R	E	E	D
S			B		E		G			E
S	N	E	E	R		B	O	W	E	R

92

E	M	E	T	I	C			A		C
M			A		O	A	K	L	E	Y
B	A	T	H	E	R	S		B		S
E			I		D	I	G	E	S	T
D	E	A	T	H		D		R		S
		D	I	A	L	E	C	T		
U		J		Z		S	H	A	R	P
S	A	U	N	A	S		E			I
U		R		R	E	S	E	R	V	E
A	G	E	N	D	A		R			C
L		D			L	E	S	S	E	E

93

W	A	T	C	H		L	U	C	I	D
	X		A		M			H		I
M	E	L	T		O	B	S	E	S	S
O			E	L	M			M		P
D	E	C	R	E	E		R	I	C	E
E		H	E	I	N	O	U	S		N
R	O	A	R		T	U	B	E	R	S
A		N			A	T	E			E
T	A	N	K	E	R		L	E	A	D
O		E			Y		L		D	
R	U	L	E	S		B	A	C	O	N

94

C	O	M	E	T		B	E	A	K	S
A			A		B		L			W
R	U	S	T	L	E		V	I	S	A
N		I			T	E	E			B
A	U	N	T		T	A	S	T	Y	
L		U		P	E	R		U		B
	O	S	I	E	R		S	T	A	R
M			M	A	O			T		I
A	Q	U	A		F	E	L	I	N	E
S			G		F		E			F
T	W	E	E	D		B	A	N	K	S

95

S	H	A	R	P		A	S	H	E	N
T		S		A			H		N	
A		P		S	H	O	R	T	L	Y
T	H	I	G	H			I		I	
U		R		A	B	R	E	A	S	T
E	D	I	T		A		K	I	T	E
S	Y	N	O	N	Y	M		L		E
	N		D			A	T	E	I	N
C	A	N	D	O	U	R		R		A
	M		L			S		O		G
B	O	G	E	Y		H	E	N	C	E

96

C		T	R	A	N	S	L	A	T	E
A		A		Z		C		W		
M	A	C	A	U		R	O	A	M	S
E		I		R	U	E		R		E
M	E	T	R	E		W	A	D	E	R
B			Y				S			E
E	N	T	E	R		C	H	A	I	N
R		O		H	O	E		M		G
T	A	R	R	Y		A	L	I	C	E
		S		M		S		S		T
C	L	O	S	E	N	E	S	S		I

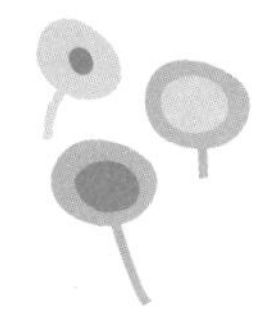

Solutions

97

C	O	V	E	N		M	A	C	H	O
A			M		A		L			W
L	A	M	P		L	U	P	I	N	E
L		A	T	O	M		H			D
E	D	G	Y		S	T	A	G	E	
R		M			H			U		G
	C	A	M	E	O		M	A	L	E
D			O		U	P	O	N		N
O	D	I	O	U	S		C	O	O	T
L			S		E		H			L
L	I	N	E	R		N	A	N	C	Y

98

S	H	A	C	K		D	R	O	O	P
I		R		I	R	A		V		U
G	L	E	A	N		R	O	A	S	T
N	A	N		D		E		L		T
S	M	A	S	H	E	S		S	L	Y
	P			E		S			I	
P	S	I		A	D	A	M	A	N	T
I		D		R		L		E	G	O
V	A	L	E	T		A	R	S	O	N
O		E		E	V	A		O		N
T	I	R	E	D		M	A	P	L	E

99

D	R	E	A	M	E	D		I		C
E		S		E		O	C	C	U	R
L	O	C	U	M		S	U	E		E
T		H		O	V	E	R	D	U	E
A	L	E		R			E			L
		W	A	Y	S	I	D	E		
P			G			N		R	A	W
A	P	P	A	R	E	L		M		E
G		E	M	U		A	L	I	V	E
A	U	R	A	L		N		N		D
N		M		E	N	D	L	E	S	S

100

B	R	O	O	M		A	G	I	L	E
Y		I		A			R		A	
P		L		T	O	R	O	N	T	O
A	S	S	E	T			W		H	
S		K		H	U	S	T	L	E	
S	W	I	P	E		O	H	A	R	E
	A	N	S	W	E	R		C		R
	R		A			C	H	O	I	R
P	R	E	L	U	D	E		N		A
	E		M			R		I		T
G	N	A	S	H		Y	U	C	C	A

101

W		M		C	O	N	S	I	S	T
A	B	A	S	H			A		A	
L		G		U	K	U	L	E	L	E
L	U	N	A	R			U		I	
O		U		N	E	X	T		N	
P	U	M	A		R		E	V	E	R
	P		C	R	A	B		O		A
	R		A			L	A	Y	E	R
V	O	L	C	A	N	O		A		E
	A		I			W	A	G	E	S
A	R	R	A	I	G	N		E		T

102

J	A	V	A			B	A	S	I	L
E			R	H	E	A		A		O
S	P	A	T	E		D		N		U
U			E	X	P	E	C	T	E	D
S	O	A	R		L		L	A	X	
	L		I	R	A	Q	I		I	
	I	C	E		Z		M	Y	T	H
M	O	U	S	S	A	K	A			A
A		R		I		E	X	C	E	L
S		R		Z	O	N	E			V
S	T	Y	L	E			D	O	P	E

103

S	U	C	H		C	H	U	R	C	H
T			A	H	A				H	
A	N	T	I		P	I	S	T	I	L
T			K				K		G	
I	N	J	U	N	C	T	I	O	N	
C	I	A			U			N	O	R
	G	R	I	N	D	S	T	O	N	E
	E		O				E			V
B	L	A	N	C	H		R	O	L	E
	L				O	H	M			R
M	A	G	P	I	E		S	U	I	T

104

T		B		H		S	K	I	E	R
E	A	R	L	O	B	E		N		A
E		O		R		N		T		C
T	O	N	G	S		S	W	E	D	E
H		Z		E		A		R		R
	B	E	T	R	O	T	H	E	D	
A		M		A		I		S		F
B	L	E	N	D		O	T	T	E	R
U		D		I		N		I		A
T		A		S	H	A	N	N	O	N
S	Y	L	P	H		L		G		C

Solutions

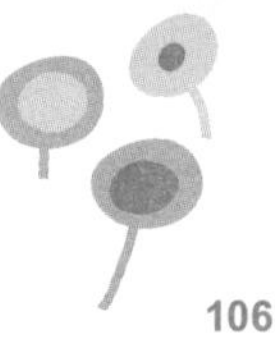

105

C	R	A	S	H		O	F	F	E	R
A			A		T	R	I	O		E
R	E	M	U	S		E	R	E	C	T
O			D		E		S			I
B	A	S	I	N	G	S	T	O	K	E
	D		A		R		C		I	
B	O	U	R	N	E	M	O	U	T	H
I			A		T		U			A
P	R	O	B	E		U	S	U	R	Y
E		W	I	R	Y		I			D
D	I	N	A	R		U	N	I	O	N

106

C	I	C	A	D	A			D		L
L			S		C	A	J	O	L	E
A	F	G	H	A	N	I		O		E
M			O		E	R	O	D	E	D
P	E	E	R	S		G		L		S
		M	E	A	S	U	R	E		
L		O		V		N	A	S	A	L
A	S	T	R	A	Y		B			E
M		I		G	O	R	I	L	L	A
B	R	O	K	E	R		E			F
S		N			E	A	S	I	L	Y

107

C	U	R	D	S		C	O	S	T	S
H		O		L		O		U		L
O	U	T	D	O	O	R		R	O	E
P				P		P		N		E
S	A	B	L	E		S	C	A	L	P
		R						M		
S	H	A	L	E		B	L	E	S	S
I		V		X		E				T
L	E	U		U	N	A	W	A	R	E
L		R		L		N		N		R
Y	E	A	S	T		S	A	T	I	N

108

C	R	A	F	T	S		A		R	
U		B			A	S	L	E	E	P
P	U	R	R		N		P		O	
O		U		C	E	N	S	U	R	E
L	A	P		A		E			D	
A	N	T	E	C	H	A	M	B	E	R
	T			H		T		E	R	A
M	A	C	B	E	T	H		Y		P
	C		O		A		B	O	A	T
W	I	G	W	A	M			N		O
	D		L		P	O	N	D	E	R

109

S	L	U	M	P		P	R	I	C	K
A			E		B		O			I
L	A	V	A		O	B	O	I	S	T
L		E	N	V	Y		T			E
O	U	R	S		W	A	S	P	S	
W		S			O			U		M
	M	O	U	R	N		U	R	E	A
G			N		D	O	M	E		N
A	D	M	I	R	E		B	E	N	T
L			T		R		R			I
L	I	N	E	N		O	A	S	I	S

110

C	A	R	D	S		B	R	I	C	K
U		A		L		L		N		E
B	A	N	D	A	G	E		S	O	T
I				K		A		U		C
T	I	L	D	E		T	O	R	C	H
		E						E		
B	R	A	N	D		S	T	R	A	W
U		P		O		L				E
S	O	D		U	N	A	W	A	R	E
E		A		S		N		I		D
S	T	Y	L	E		T	O	D	A	Y

111

	F	E	U	D	A	L	I	S	M	
H		M		A		O		L		D
A	H	E	A	D		T	H	E	S	E
U		N		D	O	T		E		O
G	O	D	L	Y		O	P	T	E	D
H			O				A			O
T	R	A	W	L		I	N	C	U	R
I		G		I	A	N		H		A
L	O	O	P	S		S	P	A	I	N
Y		R		L		E		I		T
	V	A	L	E	N	T	I	N	E	

112

T	A	M	E	D		M	I	N	I	M
A		O		W		E		E		E
S	O	N		E	N	T	R	E	A	T
T		G		L		A				R
E	N	R	O	L		L	I	S	L	E
		E						C		
L	I	L	A	C		D	E	A	L	T
E				R		E		N		A
V	A	G	R	A	N	T		D	A	N
E		I		N		E		A		G
L	U	N	G	E		R	A	L	L	Y

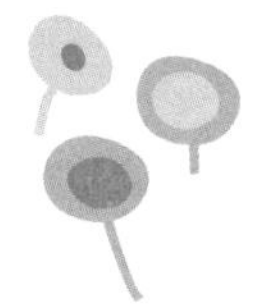

Solutions

113

S	T	R	O	P	S		S	N	I	P
T		A		I			A			I
E		V	E	L	O	D	R	O	M	E
A	C	E		L			C		O	
M	A	N	I	A	C		A	S	H	Y
	V		C	R	O	S	S		A	
F	I	R	E		G	A	M	B	I	T
	A		C				M	O	R	E
B	R	E	A	K	D	O	W	N		N
U			P			S		U		T
Y	O	B	S		C	A	S	S	I	S

114

M	A	N	A	N	A			C		A
E			N		N	E	U	R	O	N
R	E	S	T		T			Y		N
I		P	I	N	E	A	P	P	L	E
T	R	A	C	E		L		T	A	X
	A				I	C	E		N	
U	S	E		G		R	E	A	D	Y
S	P	A	G	H	E	T	T	I		I
U		R			D		U	R	G	E
R	A	T	I	N	G		D			L
P		H			E	Y	E	L	I	D

115

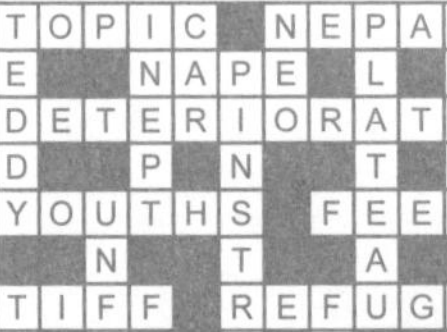

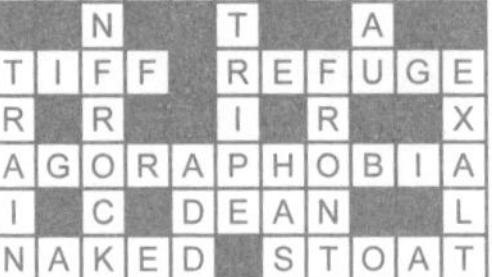

T	O	P	I	C		N	E	P	A	L
E			N	A	P	E		L		E
D	E	T	E	R	I	O	R	A	T	E
D			P		N			T		D
Y	O	U	T	H	S		F	E	E	S
		N			T			A		
T	I	F	F		R	E	F	U	G	E
R		R			I		R			X
A	G	O	R	A	P	H	O	B	I	A
I		C		D	E	A	N			L
N	A	K	E	D		S	T	O	A	T

116

A		G	U	Y	F	A	W	K	E	S
D	Y	E		O		F		I		A
A		N		G	L	E	A	N	E	D
P	R	E	V	I	E	W		D		L
T			E		T		P	L	A	Y
		V	E	R	D	U	R	E		
T	I	E	R		O		I			A
O		R		S	W	A	G	M	A	N
P	U	M	P	I	N	G		A		G
I		I		D		E		S	I	R
C	O	N	S	E	N	S	U	S		Y

117

S	T	O	O	P		T	I	G	H	T
W			P	A	W	N		E		
A	S	H	E	N		T	S	A	R	S
R			R		C		T		O	
M	E	G	A	L	O	M	A	N	I	A
	M		T		L		I		C	
F	A	M	I	L	I	A	R	I	S	E
	N		V		C		C			B
P	A	Y	E	E		M	A	C	R	O
	T			T	H	U	S			N
M	E	D	I	C		G	E	T	B	Y

118

M	E	A	N	T		A	B	A	S	E
A		P		R			R		P	
N	A	R	R	O	W		I	D	O	L
G		O		V	O	O	D	O	O	
L	A	N	C	E	R		G	E	R	M
E			O		S		E			A
D	A	W	N		T	A	S	S	E	L
	R	A	N	G	E	R		I		M
L	O	D	E		D	E	B	R	I	S
	M		C			N		E		E
B	A	S	T	E		A	N	N	O	Y

119

S	I	G	H	T		D	I	A	R	Y
H			O			O		S		O
O	M	I	T	S		N	E	H	R	U
A			P		O		N			T
L	E	M	O	N	S	Q	U	A	S	H
	V		T		C		M		K	
C	A	M	A	R	A	D	E	R	I	E
O			T		R		R			N
R	A	Z	O	R		F	A	B	L	E
K		O		I			T			M
S	N	O	O	P		F	E	R	R	Y

120

B	A	L	M			R	E	C	A	P
A		A	B	L	E		A			U
S	P	A	R			H		R	O	T
I		S	T	U	D	E	N	T		U
C	U	P		N		A		H	I	P
		E	M	B	A	R	G	O		
G	A	R		I		S		R	U	B
E		S	E	A	L	E	G	S		O
C	H	I		S			L	E	A	R
K		O		E	P	E	E			N
O	W	N	E	D			N	A	M	E

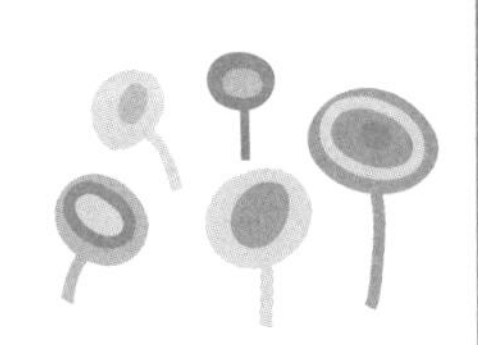

Solutions

121

A	L	E	C		S	A	C	H	E	T
W			O	A	T				A	
N	O	R	M		A	V	E	R	S	E
I			M		I		N		T	
N	A	T	I	O	N	W	I	D	E	
G	L	U	T				G	I	R	O
	A	T	T	A	C	H	M	E	N	T
	D		E		R		A			T
A	D	H	E	R	E		T	O	G	A
	I				S	R	I			W
A	N	I	M	U	S		C	A	V	A

122

B	R	I	S	K		S	H	A	R	D
A			W	I	C	K		N		U
C	L	E	A	N	L	I	N	E	S	S
K			M		I			M		K
S	O	D	I	U	M		P	O	N	Y
		A			A			N		
F	I	V	E		C	A	R	E	E	R
A		I			T		U			A
C	O	N	T	A	I	N	M	E	N	T
E		C		S	C	A	B			E
T	H	I	N	K		Y	A	W	N	S

123

A	B	Y	S	M		T		C	O	B
L			H	A	I	R	D	O		A
P	O	S	E	R		U		U		S
A		I		G		S	U	R	G	E
C	O	N	F	E	S	S		T		
A		G			P			Y		S
		L		V	A	G	R	A	N	T
C	R	E	D	O		A		R		O
A		T		C		U	D	D	E	R
N		O	R	A	N	G	E			E
T	O	N		L		E	N	J	O	Y

124

S	U	R	F			A	D	D	E	R
A			O	D	D	S		E		I
N	E	A	R			K		N		V
T		N	E	C	T	A	R	I	N	E
A	M	I	G	O		F		G		R
		M	O	N	S	T	E	R		
W		A		T		E	N	A	C	T
I	N	T	E	R	P	R	E	T		E
V		I		A			R	E	I	N
E		O		R	I	N	G			O
S	O	N	N	Y			Y	A	W	N

125

S	L	E	E	P		T	R	O	U	T
M			V			H		R		I
A	N	T	E		B	E	H	I	N	D
R		R		P		S		G		A
T	H	E	R	E		P	H	I	A	L
		A	U	C	T	I	O	N		
B	E	S	E	T		A	G	A	P	E
R		U		O		N		T		N
E	R	R	O	R	S		S	E	N	D
A		E		A				I		U
M	U	R	A	L		A	N	G	L	E

126

S	W	E	A	T		M	A	R	R	Y
T		N		I			N		E	
R		C		A	N	T	I	C	S	
U	S	H	E	R			M	A	I	D
C		I		A	B	O	A	R	D	
K	A	L	E		E		L	E	E	S
	P	A	N	D	E	R		T		T
S	O	D	A			O	V	A	R	Y
	L	A	M	B	D	A		K		L
	L		E			S		E		U
M	O	U	L	T		T	E	R	M	S

127

B		T		L		D	E	L	F	T
A	V	O	C	A	D	O		U		I
C		G		C		W	A	G		B
O	U	G	H	T		N	I	E	C	E
N		L	A	I	R		K			R
	W	E	L	C	O	M	I	N	G	
A			V		C	O	D	E		B
G	A	P	E	S		D	O	G	M	A
E		A	S	P		U		A		R
N		I		A	L	L	S	T	A	R
T	H	R	U	M		E		E		Y

128

C	O	G	N	A	C			W		S
U			A		U	P	L	I	F	T
B	I	T	T	E	R			Z		A
E			I		B	L	E	A	R	Y
D	E	C	O	Y		I		R		S
		U	N	A	R	M	E	D		
M		R		L		O	N	S	E	T
A	N	T	H	E	M		D			R
Y		A			I	C	I	C	L	E
B	R	I	E	F	S		N			N
E		N			S	I	G	N	E	T

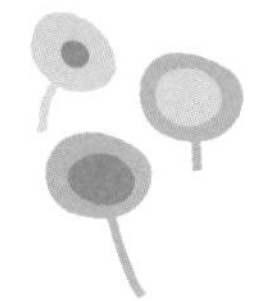

Solutions

129

M	I	S	T	S		S	E	A	L	S
E		T		O	N	E		B		P
D	R	A	W	N		N	O	O	N	E
I		L	A	S	T	S		U		E
A	S	K	S		R	E	S	T	E	D
	K		T		U		T		N	
F	I	N	E	S	T		A	D	D	S
A		I		T	H	E	I	R		C
C	O	C	O	A		G	R	A	D	E
E		E		R	A	G		M		N
S	E	R	V	E		S	C	A	L	E

130

S		R		B	E	W	I	T	C	H
T	H	E	T	A			N		H	
A		G		S	O	D	S	L	A	W
T	R	A	D	E			T		S	
U		L		D	E	L	E	T	E	
S	P	I	T		Y		P	A	R	T
	E	A	R	N	E	D		N		O
	S		U			R	O	T	O	R
D	E	F	A	C	T	O		R		I
	T		N			S	A	U	C	E
T	A	C	T	I	C	S		M		S

131

S	C	R	A	W	L		A	G	E	S
L		E		I			B			K
O		A	U	T	O	C	R	A	C	Y
O	R	C		H			A		A	
P	A	T	O	I	S		D	A	R	E
	D		S	N	A	R	E		I	
D	I	E	T		D	A	S	H	E	R
	A		R			T		U	S	E
U	L	T	I	M	A	T	U	M		G
R			C			L		U		A
N	I	G	H		T	E	A	S	E	L

132

P		L		B	A	P	T	I	S	E
A	L	O	N	E			O		C	
R		O		A	P	R	I	O	R	I
S	I	T	I	N			L		A	
O		E		S	I	T	E		P	
N	O	D	S		N		T	R	E	K
	R		M	A	K	E		A		E
	D		I			M	E	R	C	Y
B	E	D	T	I	M	E		I		I
	A		H			R	U	N	I	N
P	L	A	Y	B	O	Y		G		G

133

R	E	B	U	S		R	O	O	S	T
A		O		O		E		F		H
P	E	T	U	N	I	A		T	O	Y
I				G		L		E		M
D	A	M	E	S		M	I	N	C	E
	P		B				R		U	
U	T	U	B	E		H	E	L	P	S
N		M		X		O				H
C	U	B		T	R	A	C	H	E	A
A		E		R		R		I		F
P	A	R	K	A		D	E	P	O	T

134

B	E	A	R		A	R	C	H	E	D
U			I	R	K				L	
C	L	O	D		A	C	I	D	I	C
O			G				F		D	
L	I	N	E	N	B	A	S	K	E	T
I		U			O			O		A
C	O	N	T	R	A	P	T	I	O	N
	P		E				A			G
S	T	R	E	E	T		B	O	N	E
	I				A	I	L			N
S	C	A	R	A	B		E	X	I	T

135

C	H	E	A	T		M		R	O	W
U		N		E	L	O	P	E		I
D	O	G	M	A		U		S		S
D		I		S	A	R	D	I	N	E
L	A	N	T	E	R	N		D		
E		E			G			E		D
		E		R	O	M	A	N	C	E
B	U	R	R	I	T	O		T		A
U		I		D		T	R	I	E	D
L		N	I	E	C	E		A		L
B	A	G		R		L	O	L	L	Y

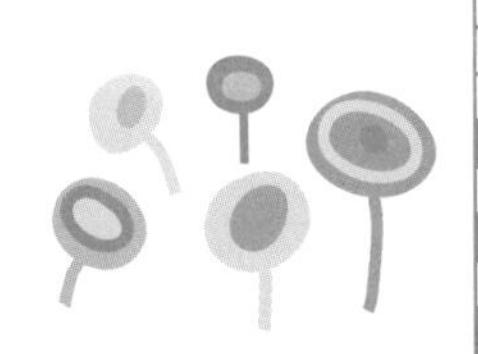

136

F	A	B	R	I	C		T		D	
A		I			A	E	R	I	A	L
C	O	S	M	O	S		O		T	
I		H		S	K	I	L	L	E	D
A	T	O	L	L			L		D	
L		P	I	O	N	E	E	R		G
	M		T			M	Y	O	P	E
S	A	M	U	R	A	I		T		N
	J		R		C	R	E	A	T	E
D	O	D	G	E	M			T		R
	R		Y		E	U	R	E	K	A

Solutions

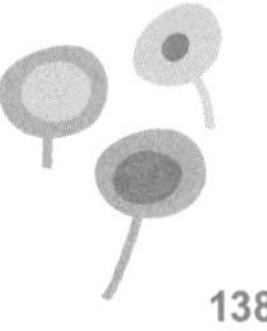

137

S		K		T		S	M	E	A	R
P	E	N	S	I	V	E		U		A
I		O		L		W		R		T
C	O	B	B	L	E	S	T	O	N	E
Y			I		N		H			L
	S	U	R	V	E	Y	I	N	G	
C			T		M		C			I
H	I	G	H	J	A	C	K	I	N	G
A		O		O		A		B		L
F		A		E	L	G	R	E	C	O
F	O	L	L	Y		E		X		O

138

S	O	R	T	S		P	E	R	I	L
T		O		T			I		M	
R		S		A	G	O	G		P	
E	S	S	A	Y			H	E	A	T
S				S	L	O	T		L	
S	A	K	E		A		H	E	E	L
	D		J	I	B	E				A
D	A	R	E			T	E	A	R	S
	G		C	A	S	H		I		S
	I		T			O		D		I
B	O	A	S	T		S	U	A	V	E

139

E	T	H	I	C	S		B		D	
X		O			O	R	A	T	O	R
C	H	O	P	P	Y		C		N	
E		P		Y	A	S	H	M	A	K
P	A	L		T		U			T	
T	E	A	C	H	E	R	S	P	E	T
	R			O		F		A	S	H
R	O	M	A	N	C	E		T		I
	S		L		U	R	S	I	N	E
D	O	R	S	A	L			N		V
	L		O		L	O	C	A	T	E

140

S	T	U	F	F		B	R	A	T	S
A		N		O		R		T		T
C	A	T	E	R	P	I	L	L	A	R
K		I		K		D		A		A
S	O	L	O		S	E	E	S	A	W
	N		A		A		R		I	
S	E	C	R	E	T		A	R	M	S
C		H		X		L		E		O
E	X	A	M	I	N	A	T	I	O	N
N		I		T		M		G		G
T	A	N	K	S		B	O	N	U	S

141

M		C		C	O	N	S	U	L	T
O	N	A	I	R			H		E	
U		R		A	R	T	I	S	A	N
S	E	E	R	S			V		V	
S		S		S	O	M	E		E	
E	A	S	T		W		R	O	S	E
	N		R	I	N	K		L		A
	G		I			O	R	D	E	R
D	E	S	P	A	I	R		H		N
	L		L			A	G	A	V	E
J	A	V	E	L	I	N		T		D

142

L	O	A	N	S		S	H	O	R	T
O		Y		T		C		V		R
C	O	R	D	O	B	A		E	X	E
A				R		L		R		A
L	A	T	H	E		P	L	A	I	D
		E						L		
W	I	N	C	E		S	A	L	V	E
A		A		X		Q				L
V	A	N		T	R	U	F	F	L	E
E		C		O		A		E		G
R	O	Y	A	L		D	I	Z	Z	Y

143

S	N	A	C	K		Z		P	I	T
T				H	E	A	V	E		A
E	X	T	R	A		I		R		X
P		W		K	A	R	A	C	H	I
P	R	O	F	I	L	E		O		
E		T			I			L		T
		I		M	A	S	S	A	G	E
C	O	M	P	O	S	T		T		N
L		I		U		A	M	E	N	D
O		N	A	T	A	L				E
G	I	G		H		L	I	G	E	R

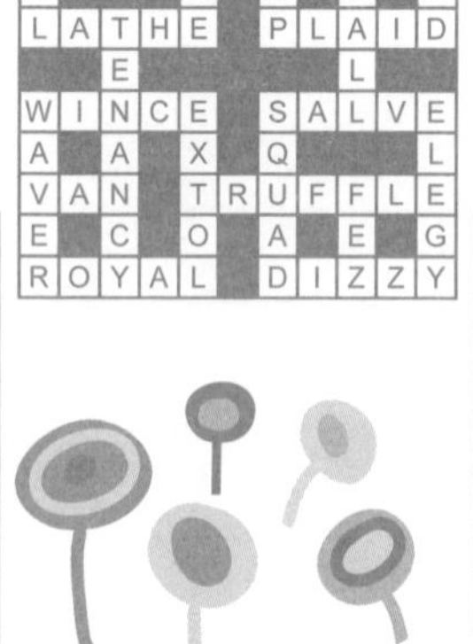

144

C	A	U	S	E		O	A	S	I	S
A			E		D		D			L
T	U	R	T	L	E		L	O	R	E
K		H			X		I			D
I	N	E	V	I	T	A	B	L	E	
N		U		K	E	G		Y		B
	I	M	P	E	R	A	T	I	V	E
S			A		I			N		A
M	E	S	S		T	A	R	G	E	T
U			S		Y		O			I
G	A	L	E	S		A	D	O	P	T

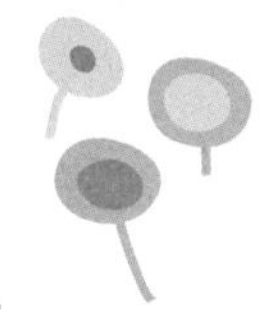

Solutions

145

K	E	B	A	B		A	B	A	S	H
N			V	A	I	N		R		E
E	L	V	E	R		T	A	M	E	S
E			R		S			E		S
L	O	O	S	E	C	H	A	N	G	E
		M		G	O	A		I		
R	E	N	E	G	O	T	I	A	T	E
E		I			P		D			I
S	O	B	E	R		O	I	L	E	D
I		U		U	N	D	O			E
T	Y	S	O	N		E	T	H	E	R

146

O	U	T	O	F	T	U	N	E		C
		R		E		N		G		U
A	G	A	I	N		D	R	Y	E	R
S		I		C	U	E		P		I
S	I	N	G	E		R	A	T	I	O
I			E				D			S
S	K	I	M	P		C	O	R	G	I
T		N		A	I	R		E		T
A	S	C	O	T		E	S	S	A	Y
N		U		H		E		I		
T		R	E	S	I	D	E	N	T	S

147

S	A	L	E	S		F	L	O	S	S
H			Y			E		V		E
R	U	L	E		A	M	P	E	R	E
E		O		S		I		R		D
D	E	N	S	E		N	E	W	L	Y
		G	A	R	N	I	S	H		
F	O	R	G	E		S	P	E	N	T
A		A		N		T		L		U
C	A	N	C	A	N		A	M	E	N
E		G		D			G			I
T	H	E	R	E		B	O	G	U	S

148

B	R	E	W	S		C	R	E	S	S
E		L		A	P	E		R		I
B	E	F	O	G		L		A	N	N
O			V	I	N	E		S		U
P	L	E	A	T		B	L	E	S	S
		Q		T		R		R		
S	C	U	B	A		A	I	S	L	E
A		A		R	O	T	A			A
M	A	T		I		I	N	T	E	R
B		O		U	F	O		I		L
A	R	R	A	S		N	A	P	P	Y

149

S	Y	R	I	A		K	A	B	U	L
C		A		C			B		S	
A	R	D	O	U	R		A	D	E	N
L		I		T	O	R	N		U	
P	R	O	P	E	L		D	U	P	E
E			R		L		O			L
L	A	T	E		B	O	N	N	I	E
	R		S	W	A	B		A		M
R	O	M	E		R	E	C	I	T	E
	M		N			Y		V		N
H	A	I	T	I		S	H	E	E	T

150

S	H	O	W	N		O	P	I	U	M
E			H		E		O			A
D	U	M	A		D	R	I	V	E	R
U		A	L	O	E		L			E
C	O	N	E		L	A	U	D	S	
E		I			W			E		S
	S	C	R	E	E		S	M	E	W
S			E		I	N	T	O		A
O	B	S	E	S	S		A	B	U	T
U			V		S		G			H
P	O	W	E	R		H	E	D	G	E

151

E		F		H		L	I	M	I	T
A	G	I	T	A	T	E		I		A
G		N		R		V		N		I
E	L	E	C	T	R	I	C	I	A	N
R			A		H		H			T
	F	O	R	G	I	V	I	N	G	
C			V		N		P			B
U	N	N	E	C	E	S	S	A	R	Y
I		A		U		A		R		W
N		T		S	I	N	A	T	R	A
G	R	O	U	P		D		Y		Y

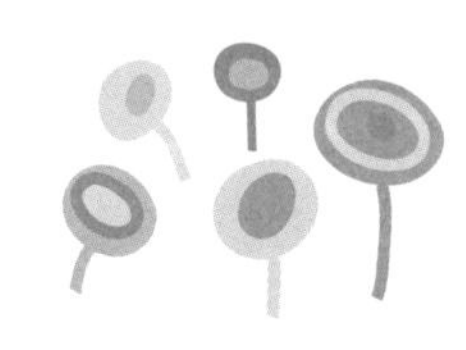

152

	D	A	L	A	I	L	A	M	A	
G		T		L		I		A		P
R	E	L	I	T		M	A	N	S	E
A		A		A	L	B		N		N
V	I	S	O	R		O	K	A	P	I
I			I				O			N
T	A	B	L	E		S	I	G	N	S
A		U		L	A	W		L		U
T	E	R	S	E		A	T	O	L	L
E		M		C		R		O		A
	P	A	N	T	O	M	I	M	E	

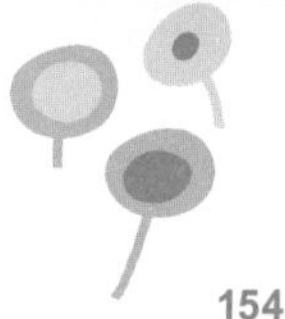

Solutions

153

K	E	Y	P	A	D			N		B
Y			O		R	E	T	I	N	A
L	O	T	S		A			N		B
I			T		G	R	I	E	V	E
E	A	S	E	L		O		V		L
		T	R	A	I	P	S	E		
O		E		K		E	T	H	E	R
B	O	W	L	E	R		U			O
E		A			O		P	E	G	S
S	T	R	A	T	A		O			E
E		D			M	O	R	R	I	S

154

C	U	F	F	S		C	U	P	I	D
U		I		H		Y		I		R
B	A	R	G	A	I	N		L	I	E
I				R		I		L		S
C	A	S	T	E		C	H	I	P	S
		E						O		
C	A	N	O	E		S	O	N	A	R
H		A		A		I				U
A	R	T		G	E	N	E	S	I	S
N		O		R		K		O		T
T	H	R	E	E		S	A	L	T	Y

155

	A	S	C	E	N	D	A	N	T	
D		P		V		U		O		A
I	R	A	Q	I		M	A	R	R	Y
S		C		C	A	B		S		A
C	R	E	P	T		O	V	E	R	T
H			E				E			O
A	M	I	T	Y		E	X	C	E	L
R		S		E	A	R		U		L
G	U	A	V	A		N	O	R	M	A
E		A		S		I		I		H
	S	C	A	T	T	E	R	E	D	

156

A	L	B	U	M		P	I	N	C	H
R		E		E	C	H	O			E
I		A	T	T	A	I	N	D	E	R
D	O	U	R		S		I			O
	V		A	S	S	U	A	G	E	D
	E		N		A		N		M	
P	R	E	S	E	N	T	S		I	
A			P		D		E	R	R	S
N	O	G	O	A	R	E	A	S		C
E			S	I	A	M		V		A
L	A	S	E	R		S	U	P	E	R

157

F	A	S	C	I	A			T		B
A			E		M	A	L	A	W	I
T	I	L	L		E			C		P
A			L		N	E	S	T	L	E
L	E	M	O	N		U		F		D
		I		A	Y	R		U		
T		R		M		O	G	L	E	D
W	E	A	K	E	N		O			I
E		C			O		U	P	O	N
A	L	L	E	G	E		D			E
K		E			L	E	A	D	E	R

158

S	I	M	I	A	N			D		O
P			C		A	P	P	E	N	D
A	M	M	O		Z			A		D
S		A	N	T	I	P	O	D	E	S
M	A	N	I	A		R			D	
	D		C	U	B	I	T		E	
	Z			P		C	O	U	N	T
S	E	N	S	E	L	E	S	S		R
O		E			O		S	A	M	E
S	H	A	D	E	S		E			A
O		R			E	L	D	E	S	T

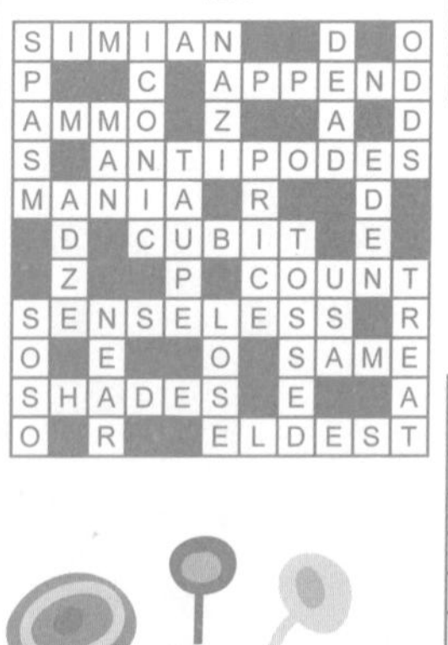

159

S		S	C	A	V	E	N	G	E	R
A		E		S		X		I		
F	R	E	T	S		A	C	R	E	S
E		P		A	L	L		L		U
T	A	S	T	Y		T	A	S	E	R
Y			E				F			R
P	L	E	A	D		S	T	A	T	E
I		S		E	M	U		D		N
N	A	T	A	L		P	R	I	E	D
		E		H		E		O		E
M	A	R	D	I	G	R	A	S		R

160

A	G	E	I	S	M		L		S	
I		M			A	S	H	R	A	M
R	E	A	P	E	D		A		L	
W		C		M	E	A	S	L	E	S
A	L	I	B	I		N	A	O	M	I
V		A		G	I	N		Y		D
E	S	T	E	R		O	H	A	R	E
S	C	E	N	E	R	Y		L		R
	R		R		A	S	P	I	R	E
F	A	M	O	U	S			S		A
	M		L		P	I	S	T	O	L

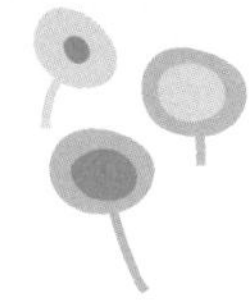

Solutions

161

P	I	A	N	O		T	H	U	M	P
A		M		R			A		A	
R		I		R	A	P	T	U	R	E
I	T	A	L	I	C		R		T	
S		B		S	A	F	E	L	Y	
H	E	L	M		D		D	A	R	K
	T	E	A	S	E	L		Y		I
	C		P		M	O	D	E	L	S
W	H	I	P	P	E	T		T		M
	E		E			U		T		E
A	S	I	D	E		S	C	E	N	T

162

M	I	N	S	K		F	I	V	E	S
A			H		S		M			L
N	O	V	A		T	R	A	U	M	A
U		A	L	O	E		G			Y
A	X	L	E		A	D	E	P	T	
L		V			D			H		D
	S	E	R	I	F		M	O	L	E
B			A		A	B	E	T		F
A	N	T	I	C	S		C	O	M	A
R			T		T		C			C
N	E	P	A	L		B	A	D	G	E

163

N	O	B	L	E		W	O	R	K	S
O			E		R		C			W
T	I	P	T	O	E		T	U	B	A
I		A			D		E			N
C	A	S	T	I	G	A	T	E	D	
E		H		N	I	B		G		C
	M	A	G	N	A	C	A	R	T	A
F			L		N			E		V
L	E	G	O		T	A	T	T	L	E
A			V		S		O			A
T	O	W	E	L		S	P	U	R	T

164

B	A	T	C	H		A	P	H	I	D
I			O		B		I			U
S	E	L	L	E	R		C	U	L	T
T		A			A	R	K			Y
R	O	T	S		S		L	O	P	
O		T	W	O	S	T	E	P		S
	L	E	O		I		D	E	C	K
C			L	Y	E			R		I
O	P	A	L		R	A	V	A	G	E
W			E		E		O			R
S	W	A	N	K		E	W	E	R	S

165

P	U	M	I	C	E		S	A	I	D
R		E		A			E			O
I		L	U	N	C	H	T	I	M	E
O	D	D		C			T		I	
R	U	S	S	E	T		L	I	L	T
	G		T	R	I	C	E		I	
Y	O	G	A		S	I	S	T	E	R
	U		T			P		H	U	E
S	T	R	E	T	C	H	E	R		C
O			L			E		O		U
W	A	R	Y		D	R	A	W	E	R

166

C	O	R	D	S		S	A	F	E	S
L		E		H		C		B		E
A	R	C		E	R	O	S	I	O	N
W		T	O	E		R				D
S	P	O	N	T	A	N	E	O	U	S
	E		C		S		U		F	
S	A	L	E	S	P	E	R	S	O	N
T				P		L	O	T		A
A	S	T	R	I	D	E		A	C	T
N		E		C		G		I		A
D	R	A	K	E		Y	O	D	E	L

167

C	A	S	U	A	L		C		M	
E		U			O	R	A	T	O	R
N	I	M	B	U	S		K		V	
O		T		N	E	M	E	S	I	S
T	O	O	L	S		A	S	T	E	R
A		T		U		R		O		I
P	L	A	I	N		I	M	P	E	L
H	A	L	O	G	E	N		P		A
	M		N		C	A	N	A	A	N
Z	E	N	I	T	H			G		K
	D		C		O	E	D	E	M	A

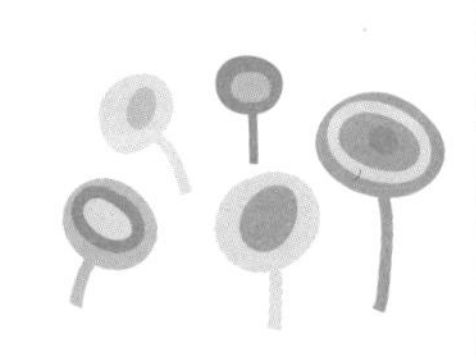

168

S	M	E	L	T			S	L	O	T
E		D		U	R	G	E			W
W		U		T		R	A	B	B	I
N	E	C	R	O	S	I	S			C
	D	E	E	R		D	O	U	S	E
	I		G				N		E	
S	T	O	I	C		F	E	L	L	
I			S	O	L	I	D	I	F	Y
D	O	L	T	S		G		T		O
L			E	T	C	H		R		L
E	M	I	R			T	W	E	A	K

Solutions

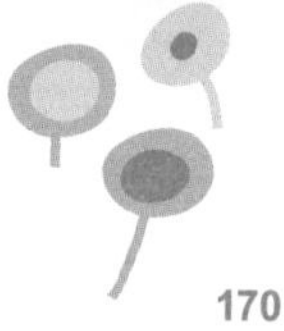

169

B	U	D	D	H	A		C	O	L	D
L		E		E			A			U
U	N	S	U	B	S	C	R	I	B	E
N		K		R			A		I	
T	A	S	S	E	L		F	U	J	I
	W		T	W	I	C	E		O	
M	A	R	E		D	I	S	C	U	S
	S		R			C		I		I
C	H	A	I	N	L	E	T	T	E	R
U			L			R		E		E
R	O	D	E		C	O	U	S	I	N

170

S	E	N	S	E		A	R	G	U	S
I			W			P		I		C
L	A	B	E	L		T	O	N	G	A
K			E		B		R			L
S	T	E	T	H	O	S	C	O	P	E
	O		P		R		H		I	
S	P	E	E	D	O	M	E	T	E	R
A			A		N		S			E
B	L	A	S	T		A	T	O	L	L
L		R		O			R			A
E	M	C	E	E		D	A	I	R	Y

171

M	A	L	T	A		C	A	T	E	R
O			H			R		R		I
S	P	O	O	F		A	M	A	S	S
E		P	R	A	N	G		N		E
S	I	E	N	N	A		T	S	A	R
		R			C			P		
L	E	A	D		R	A	D	I	U	S
A		T		S	E	W	E	R		P
G	U	I	L	T		L	I	E	G	E
O		O		A			G			L
S	A	N	D	Y		A	N	G	E	L

172

P	R	O		B	A	N	G	L	E	S
I		C		R			L			O
P		C	H	A	R	L	A	T	A	N
E	M	U		K			S		S	
S	O	R	B	E	T		S	A	L	E
	R		A	D	O	R	E		E	
B	A	I	L		G	O	S	P	E	L
	S		L			T		A	P	E
A	S	S	A	I	L	A	N	T		T
L			S			T		I		U
P	R	O	T	E	G	E		O	A	P

173

C	A	N	D	I	D		O		M	
O		E			O	U	T	L	A	W
G	L	U	M		N		I		N	
N		T		B	E	E	S	W	A	X
A	R	E		O		R			G	
C	E	R	E	M	O	N	I	O	U	S
	F			B		I		R	A	N
D	E	P	L	E	T	E		D		E
	R		E		I		H	E	R	E
D	E	M	A	N	D			A		Z
	E		F		E	V	O	L	V	E

174

S	L	I	D	E		C	A	C	H	E
N			E			A		O		N
A	R	A	B		A	D	O	R	E	D
C		B	I	B		U		P		U
K	Y	O	T	O		C	A	U	S	E
		R		N	E	E		S		
T	W	I	C	E		U	L	C	E	R
E		G		L		S	O	L		I
P	A	I	N	E	D		R	E	E	F
I		N		S			R			L
D	R	E	G	S		K	Y	L	I	E

175

A	V	O	I	D		O	P	E	R	A
N		N		E			A		E	
T	E	A	C	U	P		R	A	C	E
A		I		C	O	A	L		U	
C	O	R	S	E	T		O	K	R	A
I			E		T		U			N
D	O	L	T		E	A	R	W	I	G
	P		F	A	R	M		E		E
B	I	E	R		Y	O	N	D	E	R
	U		E			N		G		E
A	M	B	E	R		G	R	E	E	D

176

M	E	L	T	S		A	L	O	H	A
A		A		E			I		U	
N		C		P	A	I	N		B	
T	H	E	S	I	S		T	U	R	N
L				A	C	H	E		I	
E	A	R	L		R		L	I	S	P
	P		O	V	I	D				L
F	L	E	A		B	R	O	G	U	E
	O		T	W	E	E		A		A
	M		H			S		T		S
A	B	B	E	Y		S	W	E	D	E

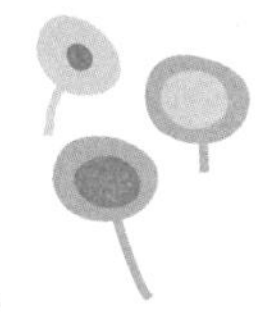

Solutions

177

R		I		A	N	I	S	E	E	D
H	A	R	E	M			L		Y	
U		O		A	S	H	A	M	E	D
B	A	N	N	S			L		L	
A		I		S	C	O	O	T	E	R
R	I	N	G		O		M	O	T	H
B	O	G	D	O	W	N		P		Y
	D		A			O	A	K	U	M
P	I	O	N	E	E	R		N		I
	N		S			S	C	O	R	N
L	E	A	K	A	G	E		T		G

178

S	H	E	D	S		I		R	A	W
A		X		P	A	S	T	A		E
L	A	T	H	E		A		T		I
T		E		E		A	T	T	A	R
E		R	A	D	I	C	A	L		
D	A	M	N		L		L	E	A	D
		I	T	A	L	I	C	S		E
P	A	N	I	C		N		N		F
U		A		O		S	O	A	V	E
M		T	E	R	S	E		K		N
A	L	E		N		T	W	E	E	D

179

C	O	W	B	O	Y		D	U	S	K
A		H		B	E	A	U			I
P		E	A	S	T		G	R	I	D
S	O	N		O		C		E		N
	B		A	L	L	O	C	A	T	E
F	O	R		E		L		P	R	Y
R	E	A	C	T	I	O	N		U	
I		M		E		R		M	E	T
A	L	P	S		W	A	D	E		A
R			A	M	I	D		A		C
Y	A	R	D		G	O	B	L	E	T

180

S	T	O	R	M		J	O	L	L	Y
E		P		O			U		I	
I		T		P	R	O	T	E	G	E
S	N	I	D	E			S		H	
M		C		D	E	S	E	R	T	S
I	M	A	M		R		T	E	S	T
C	O	L	O	U	R	S		C		E
	R		T			P	R	O	N	E
C	A	P	I	T	A	L		V		P
	L		O			I		E		L
W	E	A	N	S		T	A	R	R	Y

181

S	A	M	O	A		C	R	O	W	D
T		A		G		I		R		I
A	N	D	R	O	I	D		L	I	T
M				N		E		A		C
P	A	D	D	Y		R	A	N	C	H
		U						D		
C	O	N	G	A		A	L	O	N	G
R		G		I		R				E
I	K	E		S	W	O	L	L	E	N
S		O		L		M		E		I
P	E	N	C	E		A	L	I	C	E

182

S	T	A	G	E	S			V		V
I			E		I	N	V	A	D	E
N	A	Z	I		Z			L		N
U			S		E	S	C	U	D	O
S	U	S	H	I		H		I		M
		H	A	R	P	O	O	N		
H		R		O		O	R	G	A	N
O	R	I	E	N	T		I			E
U		V			A		S	K	Y	E
S	W	E	A	T	S		O			D
E		L			K	I	N	D	L	Y

183

S	A	L	E	S		S	P	O	I	L
P			L		L	I	R	A		E
E	X	C	E	L		P	E	K	O	E
A			P		E		C			D
R	E	D	H	E	R	R	I	N	G	S
	A		A		A		P		E	
B	U	E	N	O	S	A	I	R	E	S
U			T		E		T			H
R	A	B	I	D		C	A	B	E	R
K		A	N	O	N		T			E
A	S	P	E	N		R	E	N	E	W

184

S	U	P	E	R		D	E	S	K	S
H		I		I		R		A		I
E	V	A	P	O	R	A	T	I	N	G
L		N		T		M		L		N
F	R	O	G		R	A	I	S	E	S
	A		E		A		T		R	
S	Y	S	T	E	M		S	L	A	P
H		A		X		A		I		A
E	D	U	C	A	T	I	O	N	A	L
I		C		C		M		E		M
K	N	E	L	T		S	E	N	D	S

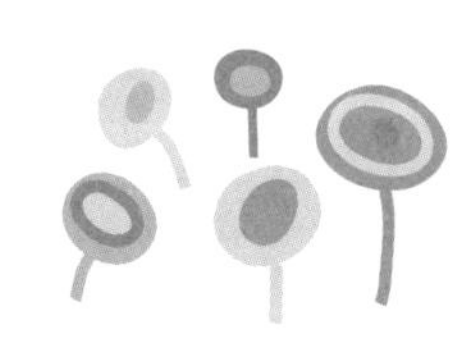

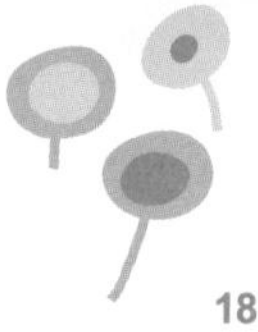

Solutions

185

H	O	E		S	I	L	E	N	C	E
I		L		U			N			E
J		B	I	L	I	N	G	U	A	L
A	D	O		L			I		P	
B	O	W	S	E	R		N	E	O	N
	M		I	N	A	N	E		G	
C	A	L	M		G	A	S	K	E	T
	I		I			U		H	E	R
A	N	A	L	G	E	S	I	A		U
P			A			E		K		L
T	S	A	R	I	N	A		I	C	Y

186

S	N	O	O	Z	E		B		D	
U		U			C	E	A	S	E	D
B	U	T	T		H		R		N	
P		D		P	O	S	S	E	S	S
O	Z	O	N	E		W		S	E	T
E		O		A	L	I		C		A
N	O	R		C		S	T	A	I	R
A	B	S	C	E	S	S		P		T
	E		H		I		M	A	L	E
E	S	C	O	R	T			D		R
	E		P		E	X	C	E	S	S

187

	A	C	A	D	E	M	I	C	S	
A		R		O		A		E		S
D	E	E	D	S		C	R	A	W	L
N		P		E	V	A		S		A
A	H	E	A	D		O	C	E	A	N
U			I				A			D
S	A	B	R	A		A	N	K	L	E
E		E		D	A	N		E		R
A	G	A	T	E		G	R	A	P	E
M		N		P		E		T		D
	W	O	R	T	H	L	E	S	S	

188

E		S		N		C	H	I	L	D
B	A	L	F	O	U	R		N		U
O		U		M		I		C		V
N	O	R	M	A		B	L	A	M	E
Y		P	O	D			I			T
	I	S	O	S	C	E	L	E	S	
A			R			N	A	Y		A
P	E	T	E	R		S	C	E	N	T
H		O		I		U		L		O
I		G		F	O	R	E	I	G	N
D	R	A	K	E		E		D		E

189

	F	L	A	S	H	B	A	C	K	
S		A		T		L		H		O
C	I	R	C	A		I	N	A	P	T
I		G		G	I	N		O		H
E	V	O	K	E		I	S	S	U	E
N			O				E			R
T	U	L	I	P		B	E	N	C	H
I		O		E	M	U		U		A
S	C	U	D	S		Y	O	D	E	L
T		S		T		E		G		F
	R	E	S	O	U	R	C	E	S	

190

E	A	G	L	E		M	U	G	U	P
	P		O		U			R		R
B	E	V	Y		N	E	G	A	T	E
U			A	D	D			N		T
C	O	W	L		E		C	U	B	E
C		E	T	E	R	N	A	L		N
A	B	L	Y		H		M	E	A	D
N		L			A	L	P			E
E	N	S	I	G	N		H	O	O	D
E		E			D		O		D	
R	O	T	O	R		C	R	I	E	D

191

G	L	U	E			E	X	P	E	L
R			A	V	O	N		R		E
A	X	I	S			V		E	L	M
N		N	E	W	N	E	S	S		O
D	O	S		A		L		S	I	N
		P	A	R	D	O	N	S		
D	I	E		R		P		T	A	G
R		C	H	A	T	E	A	U		U
O	P	T		N			I	D	O	L
O		O		T	E	N	D			L
P	A	R	T	Y			S	L	A	Y

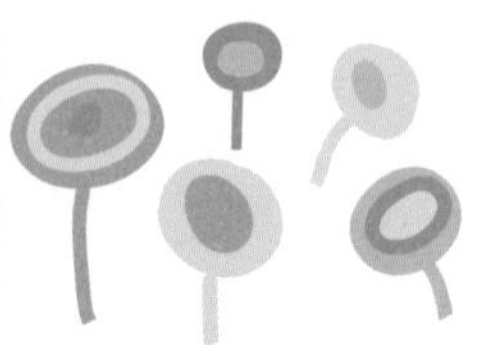

192

S	A	L	V	E	R			L		U
H			I		A	C	R	O	S	S
A	B	A	C	U	S			C		U
F			T		P	A	N	A	M	A
T	I	B	I	A		F		T		L
		E	M	U	L	A	T	E		
B		N		L		R	A	D	A	R
A	G	E	N	D	A		N			U
N		A			B	U	N	I	O	N
A	C	T	I	V	E			I		N
L		H			D	I	N	G	H	Y

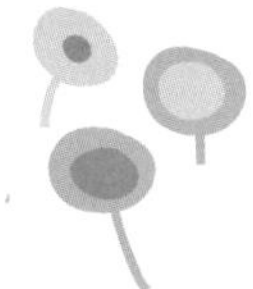

Solutions

193

B	R	I	E	F		T		C	A	D
E				I	C	H	O	R		A
C	O	M	I	C		U		I		I
A		A		H		G	E	N	U	S
M	A	R	Q	U	I	S		O		
E		E						L		C
		S		G	L	A	Z	I	E	R
M	I	N	C	E		L		N		U
I		E		L		A	T	E	A	M
S		S	K	I	E	R				B
S	E	T		D		M	A	I	L	S

194

D	A	C	H	A		S	W	A	M	P
E			O		D		H			A
C	A	R	T		E	X	E	T	E	R
A		H	E	A	P		E			A
M	A	I	L		R	A	L	L	Y	
P		N			E			E		S
	C	O	R	K	S		L	A	Z	E
C			A		S	E	A	S		T
A	V	E	N	G	E		R	E	N	T
S			G		D		V			L
H	E	L	E	N		F	A	B	L	E

195

A	U	N	T			M	O	P	E	D
D			U	G	L	I		S		O
L	O	U	T			N		E		L
I		N	U	M	B	S	K	U	L	L
B	A	D		A		T		D	A	Y
	C	E	N	T	U	R	I	O	N	
F	I	R		T		E		N	E	T
A	D	M	I	R	A	L	T	Y		E
I		I		E			O	M	E	N
L		N		S	U	D	S			E
S	T	E	M	S			S	A	L	T

196

L	I	C	K	S		B	L	O	O	M
E		R		I			E		H	
A	M	O	U	N	T		T	H	A	T
F		P		G	R	A	T	E	R	
L	E	S	S	E	E		E	W	E	R
E			T		L		R			E
T	U	B	A		L	A	S	S	I	E
	R	E	T	A	I	L		K		L
A	I	D	E		S	E	D	A	T	E
	N		L			R		T		C
P	E	P	Y	S		T	H	E	F	T

197

S	E	C	T	O	R			D		B
C			I		A	N	G	O	L	A
R	E	A	M		D			U		K
U			E	L	I	G	I	B	L	E
B	A	S	S	O	O	N		L		R
		Q		C		O		E		
B		U		H	A	M	S	T	E	R
O	V	E	R	S	T	E	P			E
G		E			L		R	E	A	R
E	C	Z	E	M	A		E			U
Y		E			S	W	E	D	E	N

198

D	I	M	P	L	E		T	E	R	M
O		A		E			R			A
M		R	E	S	T	R	A	I	N	T
E	R	E		S			M		U	
S	I	S	T	E	R		M	A	T	E
	P		I	R	A	T	E		M	
W	E	P	T		P	A	L	L	E	T
	N		A			B		A	G	E
I	S	I	N	G	L	A	S	S		D
C			I			R		S		D
E	P	I	C		I	D	I	O	C	Y

199

W	A	G	E	S			S	O	O	T
O		A		T	A	K	E			R
E		G		A			A	N	N	E
S	H	A	M	B	L	E	S			A
	O		I		I		H	E	A	D
	S		S	E	N	S	E		B	
C	E	N	T		K		L		E	
H			R	E	S	O	L	U	T	E
E	D	G	E			N		P		D
A			S	P	A	Y		O		E
T	O	E	S			X	E	N	O	N

200

B	A	S	I	C		A	B	O	V	E
A		O		O			O		I	
T		F	I	R	E	P	O	W	E	R
T	W	A	N	G			B		N	
L			D	I	A	R	Y		N	
E	L	S	E		N		T	B	A	R
	U		C	E	D	A	R			I
	S		E			B	A	N	J	O
S	T	A	N	D	P	I	P	E		T
	R		C			D		A		E
K	E	N	Y	A		E	N	T	E	R

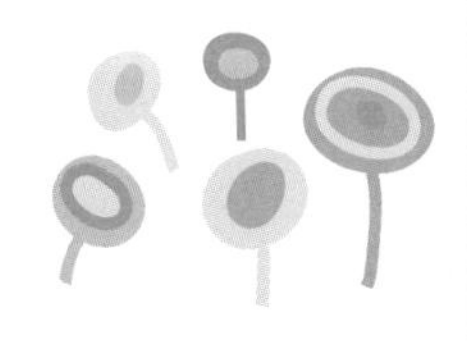

Solutions

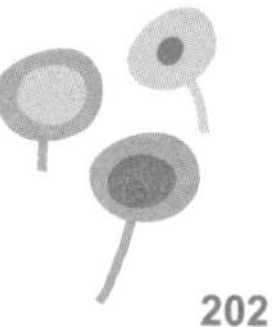

201

M	O	S	A	I	C		M		A	
I		C		V	E	R	A	N	D	A
M	A	R	T	Y	R		G		H	
O		A			T	A	N	D	E	M
S		W	A	D	I		E		R	
A	I	L	S		F		T	E	E	M
	N		U		I	R	O	N		O
C	L	I	N	I	C			D		D
	A		D		A	S	P	I	R	E
P	I	P	E	T	T	E		V		S
	D		R		E	X	C	E	P	T

202

E	M	E	R	Y		F	A	T	A	L
N			A		N		L			A
G	H	E	T	T	O		O	P	U	S
U		N			S		U			T
L	O	S	S	L	E	A	D	E	R	
F		U		E	B	B		V		S
	S	E	T	T	L	E	M	E	N	T
O			H		E			R		R
D	O	V	E		E	N	Z	Y	M	E
D			S		D		I			S
S	L	E	E	T		S	P	I	E	S

203

T	W	I	S	T		R	I	D	G	E
O			E			E		E		V
T	O	W	E	L		V		B	E	E
A			M		F	E	E	T		N
L	O	B	S	T	E	R		S	A	T
	R			Y	E	S			R	
S	E	W		P	L	E	A	D	E	D
P		A	X	I	S		G			I
L	I	D		C		H	E	A	T	S
I		E		A			N			K
T	I	D	A	L		I	T	E	M	S

204

P	R	E	S	E	T			T		A
U			P		O	B	T	A	I	N
T	R	A	I	T	O	R		T		O
U			N		T	E	S	T	E	D
P	A	N	A	C	H	E		O		E
		A	L	L		Z	O	O		
P		U		O	D	Y	S	S	E	Y
E	I	G	H	T	H		W			E
A		H		H	O	S	A	N	N	A
C	U	T	L	E	T		L			R
H		Y			I	N	D	I	A	N

205

K	I	O	S	K		S	T	E	P	S
I			H			T		X		A
R	A	R	E		B	A	K	I	N	G
O		E		C		R		S		G
V	I	G	I	L		F	A	T	T	Y
		I	M	A	G	I	N	E		
G	A	S	P	S		S	Y	N	O	D
E		T		S		H		C		R
T	O	R	P	I	D		R	E	N	O
U		A		F			U			S
P	A	R	R	Y		V	E	N	U	S

206

L	H	A	S	A		A	G	A	I	N
U		D		R	I	D		C		O
C	L	A	I	M		O	C	T	E	T
I		P		E	A	R		O		C
D	A	T	E	D		E	A	R	T	H
	S		K				R		O	
S	H	R	E	D		S	C	A	M	P
E		U		A	Y	E		R		R
E	N	N	U	I		P	O	I	S	E
K		I		S	P	A		E		S
S	O	N	N	Y		L	I	S	T	S

207

S	T	R	U	N	G			D		S
W			N		A	C	C	O	S	T
A	N	T	H	I	L	L		W		E
N			O		A	E	R	A	T	E
G	U	I	L	E		R		G		L
		C	Y	A	N	I	D	E		
A		E		G		C	O	R	P	S
S	H	R	I	L	L		M			A
P		I		E	E	R	I	E	S	T
I	G	N	I	T	E		N			I
C		K			R	E	O	P	E	N

208

R	A	V	E	N		T	I	G	E	R
E		A		E		E		O		U
B	A	N	D	A	G	E		R	I	M
U				R		N		I		M
S	I	G	H	S		S	A	L	L	Y
		R						L		
G	L	A	N	D		V	I	A	L	S
U		N		E		E				O
E	N	D		C	O	R	O	L	L	A
S		M		O		D		A		P
S	T	A	R	R		I	T	C	H	Y

Solutions

209

C	R	E	E	D		C	I	V	I	L
O			S	O	S	O		I		A
C	O	N	T	E	N	T	M	E	N	T
O			E		A			T		I
A	N	O	R	A	K		A	N	O	N
		U			E			A		
P	A	T	E		B	O	W	M	A	N
I		D			I		O			I
P	R	O	L	E	T	A	R	I	A	N
E		O		V	E	N	T			O
S	E	R	G	E		T	H	O	R	N

210

V		A	N	T	I	S	E	R	U	M
I		N		H		W		I		
E	N	J	O	Y		O	A	S	I	S
W		O		M	A	R		K		C
P	R	U	D	E		E	A	S	E	L
O			U				G			E
I	D	I	O	M		L	O	V	E	R
N		N		I	O	U		E		O
T	R	E	S	S		C	U	R	L	S
		R		E		R		S		I
I	N	T	E	R	F	E	R	E		S

211

M	O	T	O	R		F		B	I	D
O			P	O	S	E	U	R		O
R	E	C	T	O		R		I		S
T		O		T		R	O	G	U	E
A	M	N	E	S	T	Y		A		
L		S			A			D		E
		C		U	N	T	R	I	E	D
L	O	R	E	N		A		E		I
I		I		I		C	U	R	B	S
M		P	A	T	O	I	S			O
P	U	T		Y		T	E	N	O	N

212

M	U	S	T	Y		S	W	A	R	M
U			A			A		W		E
F	A	I	N	T		P	R	E	E	N
T			G		C		E			D
I	R	R	E	L	I	G	I	O	U	S
	O		R		V		T		M	
M	E	D	I	C	I	N	E	M	A	N
A			N		C		R			A
R	O	G	E	R		B	A	L	L	S
K		N		O			T			T
S	Q	U	I	B		H	E	A	V	Y

213

P		C		B		D	R	I	E	D
A	V	O	C	A	D	O		D		E
T		P		I		L		E		A
C	R	Y	S	T	A	L	B	A	L	L
H			A		L		I			S
	H	A	L	I	T	O	S	I	S	
C			A		A		O			B
H	A	N	D	G	R	E	N	A	D	E
A		A		I		V		S		R
N		M		S	K	I	L	I	F	T
T	R	E	A	T		L		A		H

214

B	U	S	E	S		A	I	R	E	S
E		P		H		B		E		E
A	N	Y	B	O	D	Y		B	A	T
C				W		S		E		T
H	O	N	E	Y		M	A	C	H	O
		A						C		
S	K	I	L	L		W	R	A	T	H
C		V		A		E				E
A	V	E		D	E	A	D	S	E	A
L		T		E		L		A		D
D	O	Y	E	N		D	U	C	H	Y

215

M	O	C	H	A		B	L	I	N	D
	N		O		D			C		Y
C	E	L	T		A	C	C	E	S	S
H			S	O	S			B		P
R	I	D	E		H		F	E	T	E
Y		R	A	M	B	L	E	R		P
S	K	I	T		O		A	G	E	S
A		F			A	C	T			I
L	A	T	T	E	R		H	U	L	A
I		E			D		E		E	
S	H	R	U	B		G	R	E	E	N

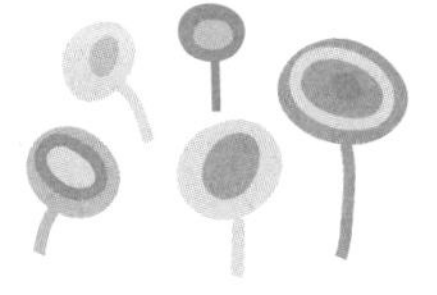

216

D	W	A	R	F			T	A	N	G
I		D		A	C	R	E			Y
S		D		N		A	E	S	O	P
C	R	E	S	C	E	N	T			S
	A	R	T	Y		T	O	A	D	Y
	F		R				T		A	
S	T	O	I	C		F	A	L	L	
T			C	A	V	A	L	I	E	R
R	O	U	T	S		L		E		A
A			L	E	E	S		G		P
P	I	T	Y			E	J	E	C	T

Solutions

217

Z		M		A	B	Y	S	M	A	L
O	P	A	L	S			P		L	
D		N		C	A	R	R	O	L	L
I	N	T	R	O			I		O	
A		R		T	A	R	N		W	
C	O	A	T		C		G	A	S	H
	C		O	W	E	S		N		A
	T		M			I	N	G	O	T
B	A	S	T	I	O	N		E		R
	V		I			C	A	L	V	E
B	E	D	T	I	M	E		A		D

218

G	A	U	N	T		S	T	O	A	T
I			U		T		O			O
G	R	A	T	I	S		N	O	R	M
G		N			E	G	G			E
L	E	N	T		T	A	S	T	Y	
E		O		A	S	P		R		F
	C	Y	C	L	E		B	E	E	R
E			O	A	F			E		I
N	E	A	P		L	E	S	S	O	N
V			S		Y		E			G
Y	E	M	E	N		C	A	R	V	E

219

B	A	B	E	L		B	O	S	S	Y
I		R		A		A		T	O	E
O		E		C	A	R	R	Y	O	N
P	L	A	N	K		G			T	
I		D		S	L	E	I	G	H	
C	A	T			A			R	E	D
	S	H	A	B	B	Y		U		E
	L			O		A	D	M	I	T
A	E	R	O	B	I	C		B		A
K	E	A		B		H		L		I
A	P	P	L	Y		T	I	E	I	N

220

S	A	I	D		C		A	M	E	N
U			R	O	A	S	T			I
P	L	A	Y		S		O	V	A	L
E		M	A	N	E		L			E
R	E	A	D		H	A	L	V	E	
B		Z			I			O		A
	J	E	A	N	S		S	C	U	T
S			L		T	U	N	A		H
H	E	E	L		O		A	L	S	O
E			E	R	R	O	R			M
D	E	F	Y		Y		E	P	E	E

221

M	A	C	A	W		S	C	A	L	P
A			R			A		L		R
P	A	P	E	R		G	U	A	N	O
L		A	N	I	S	E		B		W
E	N	R	A	G	E		B	A	I	L
		S			R			S		
C	R	O	W		V	E	C	T	O	R
H		N		B	E	L	L	E		I
I	M	A	G	O		Y	A	R	D	S
P		G		L			U			E
S	C	E	N	E		A	S	T	I	R

222

C	A	M	P		B	O	M	B	A	Y
R			L	I	E				L	
E	L	B	A		G	O	S	S	I	P
E			N				U		B	
P	A	R	E	N	T	H	E	S	I	S
U		O			E			K		A
P	A	T	R	O	N	S	A	I	N	T
	M		O				L			C
B	I	R	D	I	E		O	A	T	H
	G				R	A	F			E
C	O	P	P	E	R		T	E	L	L

223

T	H	I	E	F		W	O	R	L	D
H		R		R		A		E		I
E	L	E	G	A	N	T		P	E	T
T				N		C		L		T
A	Z	T	E	C		H	A	I	R	Y
		R						C		
C	H	A	R	D		S	H	A	R	D
L		C		U		C				A
A	S	H		S	E	A	L	I	O	N
S		E		K		N		N		T
S	C	A	L	Y		T	O	N	N	E

224

	N	A	R	C	I	S	S	U	S	
S		L		L		I		M		D
T	I	L	D	E		G	A	B	L	E
A		O		A	R	M		R		F
T	U	T	O	R		A	G	A	V	E
E			F				O			A
S	H	A	F	T		C	O	A	S	T
M		L		S	K	I		I		I
A	G	A	M	A		G	L	O	S	S
N		M		R		A		L		M
	C	O	N	S	T	R	A	I	N	

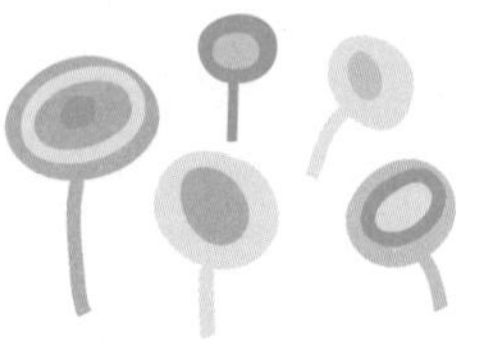